A long time ago, in a galaxy far, far away...

Following the deaths of Darth Vader and the Emperor and the destruction of the second Death Star, the Rebel Alliance proclaimed a New Republic over three-fourths of the Galaxy.

But without the thousands of Jedi Knights who formed the backbone of the Old Republic, the new confederation was a precarious one. Long years of struggle ensued, during which Imperial factions consolidated control over a fourth of the Galaxy. Whole systems became fortresses, bristling with firepower.

Then, five years after the Battle of Endor, the infamous Grand Admiral Thrawn mounted a deft assault, nearly bringing the fledgling Republic to its knees. Ultimately, Thrawn was defeated. But within days of Thrawn's downfall, surviving members of the Emperor's Ruling Council staged a stunning assault on Coruscant, and the vital Imperial System once again fell under Imperial control.

It seemed certain that a new Empire was about to emerge from the ashes of the old. That very possibility triggered a ferocious war among the numerous Imperial factions. *Who* would sit in the Emperor's throne? Who had the right — and the *might?*

Meanwhile, the Rebels were quick to seize the opportunity to sow confusion among the feuding Imperials, using captured Star Destroyers to conduct hit-and-run sorties into the war zones. During one such mission, Luke Skywalker, Jedi Knight, learns more of the Dark Side and its hold over his family. He finds hints of an ominous destiny for him and for the children of his sister, Leia. An enemy long thought defeated has returned — an individual imbued with all the power of the Dark Side itself! As long-cherished plans fall into place, new and exotic war machines move against the Republic. A Dark Empire has arisen...

Design: **Michael Allen Horne**
Additional Design: **Carol Hutchings**
Playtesting & Advice: **Dan Johnston, Jon Osborne**
Development & Editing: **Bill Smith**
Graphics: **John Paul Lona**
Cover Illustration: **Dave Dorman**
Interior Illustration: **Dave Dorman, Cam Kennedy**
Special Thanks: **Dark Horse Comics; Cam Kennedy; and especially
    Tom Veitch, author of _Dark Empire_.**

STAR WARS®
THE NEW REPUBLIC™

Published by

RR 3 Box 2345
Honesdale, PA 18431

Publisher: **Daniel Scott Palter** • Associate Publisher/Treasurer: **Denise Palter**
Associate Publisher/Sales Manager: **Richard Hawran** • Senior Editor: **Greg Farshtey**
Editors: **Bill Smith, Ed Stark** • Art Director: **Stephen Crane**
Graphic Artists: **Cathleen Hunter, John Paul Lona**
Sales Assistant: **Bill Olmesdahl** • Licensing Manager: **Ron Seiden**
Warehouse Manager: **Ed Hill**

This and all other products that take place after the events depicted in _Return of the Jedi_ are the author's vision of what may have happened. The true fate of the heroes and villains of the _Star Wars_ universe remains the exclusive province of George Lucas and Lucasfilm, Ltd.

STAR WARS

DARK EMPIRE
SOURCEBOOK

by Michael Allen Horne

A Guide to Cam Kennedy and Tom Veitch's *Dark Empire* Limited Series
for use with *Star Wars: The Roleplaying Game*

TABLE OF CONTENTS

Introduction

Full Circle

When George Lucas was gathering ideas for what would eventually become *Star Wars*, he found inspiration in such diverse sources as samurai films, Buddhist philosophy, Joseph Campbell's writings on mythology, and pulp fiction. Naturally enough, Lucas took a look at science fiction comics.

From *Flash Gordon* to *Buck Rogers* to Al Williamson's EC science fiction comics, space opera and comics have had a long, fruitful partnership. Great conflicts of good and evil, dynamic action and eye-popping panorama can all be found in these stories — the same things Lucas most wanted to bring to the screen.

In 1977, as *Star Wars* went beyond fad to phenomenon, it seemed only natural to adapt the series to the four color format that had contributed so strongly to its development. First of these was a movie adaptation; then, an ongoing series; then, a daily newspaper strip. Many of the most talented and famous artists and writers in comics, including Williamson, made their own memorable contributions to the saga.

Now, there is the latest incarnation of *Star Wars* in the comics field: *Dark Empire*. The genesis of *Dark Empire* stretches back to the late 1980's. Writer Tom Veitch and artist Cam Kennedy had gained considerable notoriety with their project, *The Light and Darkness War*. After Lucasfilm expressed interest in a *Star Wars* proposal they wrote, Veitch and Kennedy plotted out an epic set six years after the events of *Return of the Jedi*.

In 1992, *Dark Empire* was released by Dark Horse Comics and became an immediate hit. The overwhelming response from *Star Wars* fans has ensured that there will be many more adventures of Luke Skywalker, Han Solo, and Princess Leia.

The Dark Empire Sourcebook

An exciting continuation of the *Star Wars* saga, *Dark Empire* is filled with the sort of details and settings that made the original movies so enjoyable. Exotic planets and species, colorful villains, new devices and breathtaking battles fill the pages of this graphic novel. This sourcebook is a guide to the diverse inhabitants, events and settings of Kennedy and Veitch's saga.

During the writing of *Dark Empire*, West End Games was pleased to offer what aid it could to Mr. Veitch and Mr. Kennedy by providing reference material; it was only logical that a *Dark Empire* sourcebook would be a welcome addition to the *Star Wars: The Roleplaying Game* line.

Many things have changed in the six years since *Return of the Jedi*. It is less than a year after the events of the Timothy Zahn trilogy. Rejuvenated Imperial factions once again hold sway over much of the galaxy and now dare to take the battle to the homeworlds of the Republic itself. Vast armadas again bring terror and destruction in the name of a dead Emperor.

Set only days after the events of *Dark Empire*, this sourcebook provides detailed information on the elements of this saga.

How did the Emperor survive his "death" at Endor? How do the World Devastators function? What is Byss like? How did Boba Fett escape the Sarlacc? All of these questions and many more are answered in this sourcebook. This book provides full game statistics with each entry, but ownership of *Star Wars: The Roleplaying Game* is not necessary for enjoyment of this book.

Those of you who have prior *Star Wars* sourcebooks may notice that some characters have lower Force Point and Character Point totals than in prior publications. This is accurate — many of these characters have had to spend many, many points during their adventures in the Timothy Zahn novels and the *Dark Empire* comic series.

■■■Prologue

A Time Of Change

The Rebellion against the Empire was victorious with the Battle of Endor, but the conflict did not end there. The war to free the galaxy was only now beginning. No longer insurgents, the long-suffering members of the Alliance to Restore the Republic found a thousand worlds eager to join open battle against the demoralized remnants of Palpatine's Imperial juggernaut. The military, bureaucracy and COMPNOR elite could only watch impotently as system after system, sector after sector came under Republic control.

With the loss of Vader and so many talented fleet officers, things looked understandably bleak. More than that, the legions of the Empire found themselves crippled by the loss of the Emperor himself. Without the benefit of his supreme confidence and ruthless foresight, the vast Imperial war machine was paralyzed by indecision. No single individual possessed the power and the will to step forward and unite the military.

Whole squadrons and battlegroups abandoned strategic objectives to follow seemingly random dispatches from competing authorities. Vast regions of space were left defenseless as the Core systems were transformed into fortress worlds. As the war pressed on, even these worlds fell, and the remaining Imperial forces retreated to isolated backwater regions of the galaxy.

It became more apparent with every passing year that Palpatine had never intended his New Order to survive him. Warriors who had once terrorized a galaxy now found themselves embattled and divided.

However, things weren't all *chav* and *sficca* blossoms for the Rebels either. They enjoyed a newfound respect and legitimacy, and in time reclaimed nearly three-quarters of the civilized galaxy, but somehow final victory always eluded them. For every three worlds that joined the burgeoning New Republic, one remained Imperial while another declared independence. The inertia from decades of tyranny left much of the populace unused to the *responsibilities* of freedom.

Nearly as troublesome as the war itself were the internal struggles and rivalries within both the Republic and the Empire. Various factions on both sides, like Borsk Fey'lya of the Republic's Provisional Council, flirted with treason to cement their own power. With a resolution of the war perhaps years away, the underworld filled the power void, with local tyrants and crime bosses holding sway. Anarchy and disorder spread across many sections of the galaxy.

This was the case until the last of the Emperor's Warlords, the feared Grand Admiral Thrawn, returned abruptly from the Unknown Regions to organize a military force. With classic feints and distractions, he quickly secured vital supplies and troops. He also somehow gained the aid of a twisted Dark Jedi, Joruus C'baoth. In possession of the lost technical secrets of Mount Tantiss (one of the Emperor's hidden storehouses of technology, artifacts and "trophies" from his military campaigns), Thrawn was ready to launch a frighteningly effective counter-attack against a complacent Republic.

Within months, both Imperial morale and combat effectiveness reached pre-Endor levels and the "Galactic" in Galactic Empire seemed all too appropriate once again. Still, the Alliance had faced worse odds before, and soon the New Republic called upon Luke Skywalker, the last of the Jedi Knights, and his sister and Jedi-in-training, Leia, along with Han Solo, Lando Calrissian, Chewbacca, R2-D2 and C-3PO and others to put aside the work of building the New Republic in the interest of preserving its very existence.

Despite cunning and remarkable strategies, Thrawn and C'baoth faced final defeat at the hands of the Republic. The new Imperial offensive was smashed. Or should have been.

Somehow, the Empire's offensive continued, seemingly with renewed strength and many more forces than Thrawn had been able to call upon. The Empire forced the Rebels from Coruscant, capital of the Republic. Still, the Empire was plagued with factionalism and ambitious individuals vying for power. Even with these remarkable successes, or perhaps because of them, the Empire again disintegrated into several factions, engaging in a petty fratricidal power struggle.

During this time, the Rebels fought as best they could. Using Star Destroyers captured at the Battle of Endor, the Rebellion struck at the heart of the Empire, stirring even further dissension. During one of these missions, the Rebels learned that the Empire had changed. It had reformed, each faction working together, all swearing loyalty to an unseen master.

Luke Skywalker allowed himself to be captured by the Empire, and he was taken to the mysterious planet of Byss, deep in the Galactic Core. Here, Luke learned that the worst fear of the Alliance had come true: the Emperor had returned!

The Emperor has prepared for battle on many fronts. He created the horrific World Devastators, unleashing them against the Calamari homeworld itself. He has also dedicated himself to turning Luke Skywalker to the Dark Side — to making young Skywalker his loyal servant, as his father was before him.

In the tumultuous events that followed, the Emperor's grandest plans were brought to fruition as the Rebel Alliance fought a desperate struggle against a seemingly immortal foe; a struggle that brought Luke Skywalker and Princess Leia Organa Solo face-to-face with the Emperor in a final confrontation that will affect the fate of the galaxy for years!

STORMING OVER THE BATTLEMENTS, THE SEA COMMANDOS MEET THEIR FIRST OPPOSITION-- IMPERIAL STORMTROOPERS!

STANG! FIGURES THESE GUYS WOULD BE ON BOARD!

Why Do We Fight

the Empire?

1. **Because it is not legal.** As a government, it betrays the trust given it as successor to the Old Republic. It is unresponsive to the wishes of the beings it governs. It ignores their needs and oppresses them when they resist its tyranny. As such, it invalidates the purpose of a galactic government as initially stated: to serve the sapient life of the galaxy. There have been no new elections since that of *President* Palpatine. *Emperor* Palpatine and his Empire have no legal authority.

2. Because it is not moral. As a dictatorship without genuine accountability, it uses force to maintain its reign of terror over the citizenry. It levies taxes without fair and due respect for the abilities and needs of its subjects. It inflicts suffering to maintain a war economy without parallel in history. It discriminates against non-Humans. It destroys and wantonly pollutes the worlds that inhabit its sphere of domination. It is an object of hatred and fear to all who live in its sphere of influence.

3. Because it is not socially responsible. As a force of totalitarianism, it suppresses free inquiry and communication. It arbitrarily censors and murders all who do not accept the standards of normality inflicted by the "New Order." It by force tries to erase the sacred diversity that we have been provided with by nature. It has banned or eradicated histories and cultural practices of numerous societies. It has a perverse hunger for conformity.

4. Because it is not tolerant. As a force of conquest, it invades and enslaves civilizations that lie outside its natural sphere for its own greed and lust for power. It maintains a state of permanent war to expand its realm, regardless of political, cultural or philosophical concerns of those involved. It is a threat to all.

5. Because it is must be stopped. As a military entity, it has been defeated in the past, can be defeated presently and must be so defeated whenever and wherever possible. The Empire has lost its top leaders. The fight against it will continue to ensure the freedom of all who call this galaxy home and who cherish the freedom of the Old Republic. It is the responsibility of all freedom-loving beings to take up arms against the Empire.

We of the New Republic are pledged to end this long night of misery. We are pledged to defeat and destroy the Empire and restore the Republic to the Galaxy in fact and in name. Those who are currently under the threat of despotism and anarchy know this: the New Republic is committed to justice and peace and we will fight to free you. Join us if you can.

DO NOT ALLOW THE DARKNESS TO RISE AGAIN.

Mon Mothma
Chandrila

Princess Leia Organa Solo
Alderaan

Borsk Fey'lya
Kothlis

Admiral Ackbar
Mon Calamari

Jenssar SoBilles
Duro

Sian Tevv
Sullust

Verrinnefra B'thog
Indriummsegh
Elom

Doman Beruss
Corellia

Senator Garm Bel Iblis
Corellia

Kerrithrarr
Kashyyyk

Kahr'corvh clan Khim'bar
Honoghr

■ Chapter One
The New Republic

Overview

From Respectable to Rebels

So much has changed in the Galaxy in a short time. Just a decade ago, the Rebel Alliance seemed to be little more than an ideal dedicated to fighting an unwinnable war against an unstoppable Empire. Most could not imagine a universe without the Empire. Then, with the Battle of Yavin, the Empire's most devastating weapon, the Death Star, was destroyed and the Rebel Alliance became more than an "insignificant rebellion."

Over the next three and a half years, the Alliance fought and fled, attacking the Empire when it could and fleeing when it could not afford to fight. At the Battle of Endor, the Emperor was killed; the Rebels hunted his loyalists to a small corner of their former domain and declared the Republic reborn.

However, it is easier to declare a Republic than to establish one. Internal rivalries and fractiousness nearly tore the fledgling Republic apart even while the Imperials united. Under the leadership of Grand Admiral Thrawn, the Empire showed how weak the Republic really was.

The Empire forced the Republic from the capital planet of Coruscant. The Rebels returned to the isolated galactic backwaters that the Rebellion operated from when the Empire was at the height of its power. Suddenly, the Republic became a Rebellion again. It is a dark time for the galaxy once more...

From Coruscant to Pinnacle Base

After New Republic troops conquered Coruscant, capital of the Empire and the Old Republic before it, most figured the long journeys from one secret base planet to another would be left far behind. During the early days of the Rebellion, when Alliance leaders feared a single central base might be compromised, they realized the importance of keeping other worlds ready to relocate to at a moment's notice.

The Rebellion had countless secret bases, ranging from the lowly outpost, to the hidden intelligence cell, to the full-fledged military base. Still, Alliance Command needed a ready list of secret worlds for potential command bases. Alliance leadership dispatched groups of Rebel scouts about the galaxy to find isolated and uninhabited planets to locate new bases on. As part of this "Project Haven," scout teams travelled to Hoth and other worlds.

Even with the Death Star destroyed, it was imperative to evacuate before any follow-up forces arrived. When Imperial scouts finally arrived at the Massassi base, they found the mist-shrouded ruins empty and silent. Meanwhile, thousands of light years away, General Rieekan was unpacking his gear on the ice world of Hoth. When that base was unexpectedly discovered by an Imperial probe droid, it was Project Haven's ready list of back-up worlds that stood between strategic withdrawal and total disaster.

With the fleet split into countless battle groups, each one journeyed to a different world. Each group relocated as necessary to throw off Imperial pursuit.

As the Rebellion took more and more territory, countless former Imperial bases came under the control of the Republic. Formerly Imperial worlds gladly joined the growing Republic, providing even more bases and military equipment. When the Republic finally took Coruscant, there were those who felt that the list of safe worlds was no longer needed. Some even suggested ceremonially erasing the files as a sign of no going back. Fortunately, wiser minds prevailed; when the unbelievable happened, they were ready. Disheartened and angry as they were, the Rebels had no time to waste before the unstoppable Imperial wave swept the capital back into its fold.

As the last of the transports made the jump to light speed, the next priority was to establish a new prime command base as headquarters to restart the war. The thousands of existing Rebel bases were unsuitable for command base duty for they were too public, too well known. If the Alliance was to continue the war, its commanders would have to hide from the Imperial war fleet. The obvious next step was to reopen the Haven files and check for a likely world. Too obvious as it turned out. Mon Mothma and the other Councillors knew all too well just how many of their secret files were compromised by the Imperial spies of Admiral Thrawn. If the Haven files were likewise exposed, then there might be remote sensors, or mines, or worse to welcome them.

Fortunately an accident of misfiling saved the day. With so many duties and responsibilities, updating the Haven list took low priority; a little judicious cross-referencing generated a list of worlds that remained unlisted and thus uncompromised. On the basis of scout reports, the Rebel Alliance selected the Pinnacle Moon, fifth moon of Da Soocha. Soon this distant world hummed with the activity of New Republic staff members. Making friends with the local intelligent species, the Ixlls, the Rebels had a new home. In only a few months, the New Republic had gone from near total triumph to outlaw status again. Fortunately, the spirit of the Rebellion remained strong: they hadn't gotten this far by being quitters, so they would only have to work harder this time.

Admiral Ackbar

Ackbar looked out across the deep green seas of Calamari. The early morning sun was just beginning to warm the crisp sea air. In some ways, it was just like any other morning on Calamari. He leaned on the railing of the temporary dock as it jutted soothingly in the ocean.

Only a few days ago there was a city here. Now there is only wreckage and spilled blood. So many dead, so much destroyed. All in the name of power... of the Empire.

The admiral took a sip from his cup of steaming *chi'ffa*. He had never known such pain and regret and ... guilt.

The old admiral's thoughts trailed back to how this had all began, with those first tentative steps into space.

It all sounded heroic and glorious. If only we'd had any inkling of what was in store for us in space.

We forced the Empire off our world once. They fought with blasters and fighters, destroying cities at will. We fought with whatever we had — kitchen utensils, industrial tools, our bare hands. We won that time.

(The following is taken from a personal communication from Arhul Hextrophon to Voren Na'al during the fighting on Coruscant)

A Rebel's Job is Never Done ...

Dear Voren,

Some times we live in! Here at Chandrila, we're still sorting out all the information from the various reports coming in. So far I concur: we've all been entirely too arrogant. We had so easily assumed that Thrawn was nothing but the death throes of some old beast. Quite the contrary.

Still, it is shocking to read your preliminary reports. After the injuries I received on Caprioril, I have nothing but time, so I have been editing some notes.

Since they released me from the hospital, I've been staying at Mon Mothma's old dacha by Lake Sah'Ot. Wonderful view. The pain isn't bad, though the surgeon won't prescribe enough pain killers. That's the problem with organic doctors: they don't listen to you when they don't feel like it.

As I was saying, I can understand how you must be feeling right now. Truly it is a dark time for the galaxy. All we can do is give our best and do what we can to preserve the New Republic. Of course, it isn't as bad as Tarim or Bahni make out. Some worlds never stopped calling us "Rebels." Still, we are so much better off than ten years ago.

We certainly have a fight on our hands, but if their behavior on Coruscant is any indication, they're draining the fuel cell at both ports. The Imperials are so eager to defeat us, yet can't cooperate once victory seems to be within their grasp.

Have you had that chance to speak to Skywalker yet? Please forward recordings ASAP. Some of my staff doesn't believe all of what they hear from the initial report you filed.

Well, enough for now. I must get some rest if I'm to meet with Captain Flin about the memorial fund.

Please give Rivoche my warmest wishes. Our prayers go with her. Don't you worry, my boy; if she isn't safe with General Calrissian and General Antilles aboard, where would she be safe? If she survived Coruscant, she can survive anything.

Yours,
Arhul

And, now we've gone through this slaughter a second time. This time, the Imperials had their so-called World Devastators to add to the carnage. This was no battle; this was a massacre. We were so unprepared. We forgot how brutal this galaxy can be.

Ackbar looked out across the ocean, spotting several cleanup crews that were already hard at work. He came here to be with his people. As the most visible Mon Calamari in the Republic government, he felt it was his responsibility to be here to help share the pain. This was his emotional burden to bear.

We've been through so much recently. The Bothans nearly took control of the Republic — and they were willing to have me be a scapegoat to do it. And now this.

The shock is just beginning to wear off. Children are so frightened they won't leave their homes. Most people are still having nightmares about those things descending from the sky and slicing cities in half.

The reconstruction will take years. We're so divided on this ... the Quarren talking about leaving for a new world. They blame us, the Mon Cals. Perhaps leaving would be for the best.

... I wonder how many of my people blame me? I'm the one who led us into the Rebellion. I wonder if they hold me responsible?

Maybe it's time to let some of the younger staff take over. Someone with more energy. I've done my best. I could do other things — posts at military academies, chairs in corporations, even some political appointments. Or, maybe just get a simple home far from the fighting and retire ... but that's what got us all into this trouble in the first place. Pretending it wasn't our problem.

Enough turbid thinking for now! There is still work to be done. We've got to pull together. A safe Republic is still the best bet for a safe Calamari.

Ackbar finished his mug of the steaming drink, as a group of city councillors approached him. *There is work to be done ...*

■ Admiral Ackbar
Type: Mon Calamari Admiral
DEXTERITY 3D
Blaster 5D+2, blaster artillery 4D+1, dodge 4D+1, melee combat 5D+1, missile weapons 4D+1, missile weapons: power harpoon 5D+1
KNOWLEDGE 3D
Alien species 7D+1, bureaucracy 8D+1, cultures 5D, intimidation 5D+1, languages 6D, planetary systems 8D, survival 4D, survival: ocean/undersea 6D, tactics: capital ships 9D, tactics: fleets 9D+2, tactics: starfighters 7D+1, value 5D+2, will power 6D
MECHANICAL 3D+1
Astrogation 8D, capital ship gunnery 7D+2, capital ship piloting 8D+1, capital ship piloting: Mon Calamari battle cruiser 10D, capital ship shields 6D+1, repulsorlift operation 5D+1, sensors 5D+1, space transports 5D+2, starfighter piloting 6D+1
PERCEPTION 2D+1
Bargain 7D, command 9D, command: Mon Calamari crewmen 11D+2, hide 4D+1, persuasion 6D, search 5D+1, sneak 4D+2
STRENGTH 3D
Lifting 4D, stamina 6D, swimming 8D+2
TECHNICAL 3D+1
Capital ship repair 5D+1, capital ship weapon repair 4D+2, computer programming/repair 4D+1, droid programming 4D+1, first aid 4D+1, first aid: Mon Calamari

5D+1, repulsorlift repair 5D+1, security 7D+1
Special Abilities:
Moist Environments: When in moist environments, Mon Calamari receive a +1D bonus to all *Dexterity, Perception* and *Strength* attribute and skill checks.
Dry Environments: When in very dry environments, Mon Calamari seem depressed and withdrawn. They suffer a -1D penalty to all *Dexterity, Perception* and *Strength* attribute and skill checks.
Force Points: 3
Character Points: 15
Move: 10
Equipment: Comlink (wired into the HoloNet), datapad, military dress uniform, standard military uniform

Luke Skywalker

Once Luke Skywalker dreamed of adventure. His mind awhirl from the latest episodes of a favorite holo-drama, he would stare at the stars in the sky of his native Tatooine wondering if he had a destiny to match that of his heroes. The Emperor was a tyrant, and his New Order must be overthrown, but to a Tatooine farmboy, it might have been in another galaxy for all he could do about it.

That was before he met Obi-Wan Kenobi. With his only relatives dead, his home destroyed and nothing left for him on Tatooine, he became Ben's student. Soon, Luke had found more adventure than he ever dreamed possible.

Ben helped Luke start down the path of the Force. In time, Luke learned much more, especially from Yoda, the Jedi Master. Amid the decaying trees and bayous of Dagobah, Luke came to a greater understanding of the Force and his unity with it. He also learned more of the Dark Side. And in the shade of a Dark Side Nexus, he began to learn the true power of darkness and its hold over his life. He had nurtured a hatred against Vader since he saw his first teacher killed.

Master Yoda told Luke that an obstruction to his training was this anger. If Luke wanted to succeed where others had failed, he must forget his hate and rage. No Jedi could ever attain oneness of spirit and correctness of action as long as the Dark Side influenced them. Unfortunately Yoda's teachings were to go unfinished.

The Emperor had come to know of Luke's power and potential. At first he wanted the son of Skywalker slain, but Vader urged turning him to the Dark Side instead. Through an elaborate trap, Vader lured Luke to Bespin, and there he revealed knowledge Yoda hadn't been able to impart yet: that Darth Vader was his father.

Vader revealed this to Luke and offered to share rulership of the galaxy if Luke would join him. Luke refused Vader, but in that battle, the young Jedi began to realize that he, like his father, could fall victim to the Dark Side if he wasn't ever vigilant.

Still, the Dark Side was tempting, beckoning the young Jedi. In the climactic confrontation aboard the second Death Star, Luke gave in to his anger and recklessness. He crippled his father in combat — but something stopped him from completely surrendering to the Dark Side. At that moment, as the Emperor tried to kill the young Jedi with his Dark Side abilities, Anakin redeemed himself, sacrificing his life to save his son's.

Luke had only a few moments to share with his father before he died, but the tragedy of his father's life still haunted him. Later, as he trained his sister to be a Jedi, as he now was, the question still haunted him. When he confronted other Dark Side servants, even the fearsome C'baoth, their powers held no appeal for him. That changed when he journeyed to Byss, in the shadow of the Empire, where he met a reborn Palpatine. There he found his most basic assumptions challenged.

Palpatine held a power over Luke that C'baoth never could. Where Luke felt concern and even pity for C'baoth, Palpatine's power seemed overwhelming. The Emperor was not a mad, deluded shadow of a once great man; he was a conscious, willing participant in corruption for its own sake. Luke apprenticed himself to the Emperor of his own free will. Palpatine was so powerful in this new incarnation that Luke felt that the only way to defeat the Dark Side was to know its ways and to find its weaknesses. Luke has chosen his destiny: to understand the Dark Side from within and to use that knowledge to conquer it.

As Master Yoda warned and Obi-Wan feared, Luke's first step down the path of darkness was like opening a portal to his most evil urges. He followed his father's path. He quickly fell under the Emperor's sway, consumed by anger and hate, and seemingly powerless to defeat the Emperor. Only the efforts of his sister Leia saved him from eternal darkness. If not for her, the Emperor might have triumphed.

Many things are crossing Luke's mind now. His need to restore the Jedi fellowship as soon as possible. The pain he caused Han and Leia. Most of all, though, is the pain of wisdom. Wisdom gained through his own near damnation. He now knows more fully the glory of the Light Side of the Force because he has also known the Dark Side's awesome power to twist and pervert. This is the nature of the Force, and those he will train must confront this themselves. How many will triumph and how many will fall?

IT'S *GOOD* THAT YOU CAME TO BYSS...YOUR JEDI POWER, ADDED TO MY OWN, HAS *HELPED* ME BREAK THE GRIP OF THE DARK SIDE.

■ Luke Skywalker

Type: Jedi Knight

DEXTERITY 3D+2
Blaster 6D+2, brawling parry 6D+2, dodge 8D+2, melee combat 5D+2, melee parry 10D+2, lightsaber 11D

KNOWLEDGE 3D
Alien species 5D, bureaucracy 5D+2, intimidation 6D, languages 4D, planetary systems 5D+1, scholar 5D, streetwise 6D+1, survival 7D+2, value 5D, willpower 8D

MECHANICAL 4D
Astrogation 7D, beast riding 5D+1, beast riding: Tauntaun 6D+1, communications 4D+1, repulsorlift operation 8D+1, repulsorlift operation: airspeeder 8D+2, starfighter piloting 8D+1, starfighter piloting: X-wing 10D+1, starship gunnery 8D+1, starship shields 7D+1

PERCEPTION 3D
Bargain 5D, command 8D+1, con 4D, hide 7D, search 6D, sneak 7D+1

STRENGTH 3D+2
Brawling 6D+2, climbing/jumping 7D+2, lifting 6D, stamina 8D+2

TECHNICAL 3D
Computer programming/repair 5D+2, droid programming 6D+1, droid repair 6D+1, droid repair: astromech 7D+1, first aid 5D+1, lightsaber repair 9D, repulsorlift repair 7D+1, security 5D+1, starfighter repair 6D+1

Special Abilities:
Force Skills: Control 13D+1, sense 11D+1, alter 10D+2
These are only some of the powers that Luke has so far demonstrated:
Control: Absorb/dissipate energy, accelerate healing, control pain, detoxify poison*, emptiness, enhance attribute*, hibernation trance, reduce injury, remain conscious, resist stun, short-term memory enhancement*
Sense: Combat sense*, danger sense*, life detection, life sense, magnify senses, receptive telepathy, sense Force
Alter: Injure/kill, telekinesis

Control and Sense: Farseeing*, lightsaber combat, projective telepathy
Control and Alter: Control another's pain*, inflict pain, Force harmony
Control, Sense and Alter: Affect mind, doppleganger, telekinetic kill*
Sense and Alter: Dim other's senses
*These powers are described in the *Dark Force Rising Sourcebook.*
This character is Force-sensitive.
Force Points: 6
Dark Side Points: 6
Character Points: 33
Move: 10
Equipment: Lightsaber (5D damage), comlink, cloak

Leia Organa Solo

Leia's life has changed so much in just the past year. A few years ago, the Rebellion was the totality of her life. Now, her responsibilities continue to grow ... wife, Jedi Knight, and mother are new roles that she has taken on. So little time for husband and family, she has had to steal what time she could to raise young Jacen and Jaina. And soon there will be a new member of the family. Still, she is called away too often to fight the important battles only she can fight. Leia finds small comfort in the knowledge that the twins are secure with Winter on a distant nursery world, protected by her Noghri.

Her Noghri ... she musn't think of them that way. There has been too much of that in her family already. She was grateful that the Noghri had allied themselves with her and the Republic. These missions are what she must do to create the kind of galaxy she wants her children to live in. A galaxy where Dark Side followers aren't eager to claim them and change them into mindless slaves, as C'baoth and Palpatine had planned. She hopes that someday her children will understand that she had to make this sacrifice to make the galaxy safe for every child.

One thing that has given her added hope was a chance meeting with an old woman in the alleys of Nar Shaddaa. This was no ordinary old woman; it was the legendary Vima-Da-Boda, Jedi Knight. Vima called out to Leia as she walked by and told her of the light that glowed within her. After presenting Leia with the gift of her own lightsaber, she disappeared; with luck this will not be the end, but the beginning, of her time with the Jedi woman. Leia hopes to gain a new perspective on the Force.

Luke was a wonderful teacher, but he'd kept to himself so much of late. The fate of Darth Vader hung about him at times, never more than during his most recent visit to Coruscant and his time on Byss. She was as much Anakin's child as he, but Luke felt a much stronger presence. It had frightened her on Byss to see him so

helpless. She hadn't saved him; they had saved each other. Perhaps they had saved the future as well. With the Holocron, they would finally see to the rebirth of the Jedi. There is hope in the galaxy again.

◾ Princess Leia Organa Solo

Type: Young Senatorial
DEXTERITY 3D
Blaster 9D, blaster artillery 4D+1, brawling parry 5D+2, dodge 8D, grenade 4D+1, lightsaber 5D+2, melee combat 6D+2, melee parry 6D+1, running 5D, vehicle blasters 4D
KNOWLEDGE 4D
Alien species 8D, bureaucracy 9D+2, bureaucracy: New Republic Provisional Council 9D+1, cultures 9D+1, languages 7D+2, law enforcement 7D+1, planetary systems 9D+1, streetwise 7D, survival 8D, value 6D+1, willpower 7D+2
MECHANICAL 2D+2
Astrogation 5D, beast riding 4D+1, communications 5D+2, hover vehicle operation 3D+2, repulsorlift operation 5D+1, sensors 4D+2, space transports 3D+1, starfighter

piloting 6D, starship gunnery 6D+1, starship shields 5D+2

PERCEPTION 3D+1
Bargain 7D, command 11D, con 6D, gambling 5D, hide 7D, persuasion 9D, persuasion: debate 10D+1, persuasion: oration 11D+2, search 6D, sneak 7D+1

STRENGTH 3D
Brawling 4D+2, climbing/jumping 5D+1, stamina 7D, swimming 5D+1

TECHNICAL 2D
Computer programming/repair 4D+2, demolition 3D+1, droid programming 5D, first aid 7D, security 6D, space transports repair 4D+1

Special Abilities:
Force Skills: Control 5D+1, sense 4D+2, alter 3D
These are only some of the powers that Leia has so far demonstrated:
Control: Absorb/dissipate energy, control pain, resist stun
Sense: Danger sense*, life detection, life sense, magnify senses, receptive telepathy
Alter: Telekinesis
Control, Sense and Alter: Force harmony
* Described in the *Dark Force Rising Sourcebook*.
This character is Force-sensitive.
Force Points: 3
Dark Side Points: 1
Character Points: 10
Move: 8*
* Due to pregnancy; normally 10
Equipment: Lightsaber (5D damage), Jedi Holocron, comlink, blaster pistol (4D damage)

Han Solo

Being born a Corellian was enough to guarantee anyone an interesting life. That was the saying. Han had never had much use for sayings, but he couldn't argue with this one. He had enough interestingness about him to rub off on most of his friends as well.

It's kind of strange how life can be so "coincidental." Ever since Han joined up with the Rebellion, he seemed to be spending more and more time trying to persuade his old smuggling buddies to help in the war effort. Han never figured that the Rebellion would have to rely on his old friends, Shug Ninx and Salla Zend, to help save the galaxy, but when everything was on the line, it came down to his old buddies on Nar Shaddaa. They were the only ones who could get them into the Galactic Core to save Luke. Funny how life's like that sometimes.

Of course, Han's life had been funny like that before. Han's stint in the military was brief enough, and brought to an inglorious end when he allowed a Wookiee slave to escape (some say he freed the Wookiee). At least Han escaped with his honor. Han found himself adrift, aimless, with only the Wookiee for company. Then Old Mako got him out of his funk and into a job as a smuggler, operating out of Nar Shaddaa.

Those old days are a bit of an embarrassment to him now, but that's where he learned a lot about smuggling and life in general. Of course, he got grief for the Wookiee following him around, but it beat hiring a bodyguard. It was Mako who took him under his wing and showed him the upside of the Corellian Sector on Nar Shaddaa. This was how he met Shug and Salla.

Salla. Seeing her again really brought back some memories for the old smuggler. That was a long time ago — a different place, a different time. Still, the wounds are there for both of them. It had been so simple at first — competitors, then business partners, then something a lot more. Of course, it couldn't have lasted forever. When Salla had that mishap and wanted to settle down, Han felt things were moving too fast. Responsibility and stability — those were part of another life. One he'd left behind.

Han went where his luck took him; he bounced from one side of the galaxy to the other. He got arrested and shot at in most of the systems he visited. Eventually, he got into debt to Jabba. To get out from under that, he'd had to take a few passengers. That opened up a new life entirely. Behind all the cynicism and doubt, there was something that remained true to his old self. Without even knowing why, he threw in with the Rebels to see where it took him.

Now, Han's gone respectable, at least as much as his nature will allow. Of course, that respectability constantly seems to get him into trouble. He found he could become a husband and a father. Suddenly, being settled down didn't seem all that bad.

Of course, marrying one of the leading diplomats of the New Republic has kept him busy. If it's not leading a diplomatic mission, it's fighting off the last of the Emperor's Grand Admirals. In between escapades, he tries to find time to visit his infant son and daughter.

Now, things have gotten dangerous again. The Empire's back and it's stronger than ever. Then there's Luke and this business about the Emperor and the Dark Side. Han can say that he misses the wide-eyed kid he met a decade ago. He loves Luke like a brother, but he feels that his dabbling in the Force is dangerous — not just to Luke himself, but to Leia and the children.

Han had watched Luke grow with the Force. There was something, just under it. A shadow that made Han's blood run cold. He thought he knew Luke like an old reliable power coupling, but when Luke had shown up so changed, Han wondered if the old Luke was even still there. And if not, what might Han have to do to save his family? Luke may have come back from the Emperor's sway, but for how long? Is Luke really in control? Will Han have to fear for his children again — might he even, at some desperate hour, be forced to choose between his brother-in-law

and his children?

Han Solo has much to think on at this time. He hopes things might get dull, just for a little while. With the Emperor dead (again!), he might just get such a chance.

■ Han Solo

Type: Smuggler
DEXTERITY 3D+1
Blaster 8D+2, blaster: blaster rifle 5D+1, blaster: heavy blaster pistol 10D+1, blaster artillery 6D+1, brawling parry 8D, dodge 8D+2, dodge: energy weapons 9D+2, grenade 6D+1, melee combat 6D+1, melee parry 5D+1, missile weapons 6D+1, pick pocket 5D+2, running 5D+2, thrown weapons 5D+1, vehicle blasters 6D+1
KNOWLEDGE 2D
Alien species 7D, bureaucracy 7D, business 6D, business: smugglers 7D+2, cultures 6D+1, intimidation 8D, languages 6D, law enforcement 6D, planetary systems 8D, streetwise 9D, streetwise: Jabba the Hutt's organization 10D+1, survival 8D, value 6D, willpower 6D+2
MECHANICAL 3D+2
Astrogation 9D, beast riding 5D+2, beast riding: Tauntaun 6D, capital ship gunnery 6D+2, capital ship piloting 8D+2, capital ship shields 6D+2, communications 5D+2, ground vehicle operation 5D+2, repulsorlift operation 8D, sensors 6D, space transports 8D, space transports: YT-1300 transports 12D, starfighter piloting 7D+2, starship gunnery 9D, starship shields 7D+1, swoop operation 8D+2
PERCEPTION 3D
Bargain 8D+1, command 8D, con 8D+1, forgery 5D, forgery: ships IDs 7D, gambling 8D+1, hide 8D+2, persuasion 6D+1, search 6D+1, sneak 6D
STRENGTH 3D
Brawling 7D+2, climbing/jumping 6D, lifting 5D+2, stamina 8D, swimming 4D+2
TECHNICAL 2D+2
Blaster repair 5D, computer programming/repair 7D+1, demolition 6D+2, droid programming 6D+1, first aid 3D+2, ground vehicle repair 5D+2, repulsorlift repair 7D, security 7D+1, space transports repair 7D+2, space transport repair: YT-1300 transports 9D+2, starship weapons repair 5D
Force Points: 1
Character Points: 14
Move: 10

Equipment: Modified heavy blaster pistol (5D+2 damage), comlink

Chewbacca

After Admiral Ackbar, Chewbacca is perhaps the most famous alien in the New Republic (even if he isn't an official part of the ruling council). Chewbacca has done much to increase awareness of the sophisticated and ancient society of his people, the Wookiees of Kashyyyk. Thanks to his highly visible presence, most people no longer consider Wookiees to be savages. Chewbacca has, in his own way, helped eliminate much of the prejudice against non-Humans fostered by the Empire.

From slave, to smuggler, to Republic hero, Chewie has always stood by Han Solo. Long ago, Chewbacca regularly saved his life in the back alleys of Nar Shaddaa. These days, Chewbacca seems to have to save Han as often as ever, but now the fate of the galaxy is at stake instead of a cargo of dreamvenom snakes or frozen flangth husks. Now that Luke Skywalker and Princess Leia Organa Solo are part of his honor family, Chewie seems to get involved in countless other quests. Whether it's trying to release the Noghri from their servitude to the Empire, protecting Leia and her children from the Empire and Joruus C'baoth, or trying to save Luke Skywalker from the Emperor, Chewie is always in the thick of things.

The events of recent months have reminded Chewbacca of the dangers his people face. The attack on Calamari worries him. If one Rebel world is victimized, why not another? If the Empire was getting back in business, then they would want more slaves. Now, Chewie realizes that there is a good chance of some new super

STAR WARS

YRRAAWNNON!

AS THE MILLENNIUM FALCON BLASTS AT TWICE THE SPEED OF LIGHT TOWARD THE CALAMARI BATTLEFIELD, HAN SOLO AND THE WOOKIEE CHEWBACCA SPLICE ARTOO-DEETOO INTO THE FALCON'S COMMUNICATIONS SYSTEM--

TEEK-BEEP... BIP BIP BREET BWEET!!

PERCEPTION 2D
Bargain 5D+1, command 5D+2, gambling 5D+1, hide 4D+2, search 4D+1, sneak 4D+2
STRENGTH 5D
Brawling 11D, brawling: martial arts 6D, climbing/jumping 8D, lifting 11D, stamina 10D, swimming 7D
TECHNICAL 3D+1
Blaster repair 5D+2, bowcaster repair 6D, computer programming/repair 9D, demolition 6D, droid programming 8D, droid repair 7D+2, first aid 5D+1, repulsorlift repair 7D+1, security 7D+2, space transports repair 10D+2, space transports repair: YT-1300 transports 12D+2
Special Abilities:
Strength skills:
Brawling: martial arts: Chewie learned the rudiments of the Noghri martial arts style. He gets +2D when fighting somebody without this specialization and causes *Strength* +1D+2 damage. See page 94 of the *Dark Force Rising Sourcebook* for more information.
Berserker Rage: Chewie gains +2D to *Strength* when brawling in *berserker rage*. See page 137 of *Star Wars: The Roleplaying Game, Second Edition* and page 124 of *Star Wars Gamemaster Handbook.*
Climbing Claws: +2D to *climbing*.
Force Points: 1
Character Points: 8
Move: 13
Equipment: Bowcaster (4D damage), ammo, droid tool kit, starship tool kit, waist pouch

weapon someday appearing over Kashyyyk. It is imperative to defeat the Empire once and for all.

Chewie hasn't seen his family in some time now and misses them. Now that the Emperor is dead, hopefully the fighting will wind down enough that he can go to visit them. He might even bring his friends with him: he would especially like Luke to meet his family. Luke has always been a good friend, and he could use something to get his mind off his troubles of late. And there is nothing like homemade Xachibik broth to make you feel like a new person.

■ Chewbacca
Type: Wookiee
DEXTERITY 2D+2
Blaster 7D, bowcaster 10D, brawling parry 8D+1, dodge 7D, grenade 5D+1, melee combat 8D, melee parry 8D, vehicle blasters 7D
KNOWLEDGE 2D
Alien species 7D+1, bureaucracy 4D+2, business 5D+1, cultures 3D+2, languages 6D, planetary systems 8D, streetwise 7D, survival 7D+2, value 8D
MECHANICAL 3D
Astrogation 8D+2, beast riding 4D, communications 5D+1, repulsorlift operation 7D+2, sensors 7D, space transports 8D, space transports: YT-1300 transports 11D+2, starship gunnery 8D, starship shields 7D, walker operation: AT-ST 4D+2

General Lando Calrissian

Lando had played many high risk games before, but retaking his commission in the New Republic had to be one of the bigger gambles of his life. With the Empire on a roll, the galaxy in the pot, and the chances for a private operator looking sorrier and sorrier every day, what else could he do? It was more than just the abstract idea of freedom, or even the losses his projects had taken. From the takeover at Bespin, to the fracas on Nkllon, Lando just saw the Empire winning and winning. And nothing, nothing got to a gambling man more than seeing some dumb brute cleaning up without any finesse. It was the chance that he could make a difference that made the risk all the sweeter.

He'd felt differently back in the old days, palling around with Han and Rik and the others. Those had been wild times, but Lando liked the sense of building something. At first, it was the experience of building a minor fortune over a few days at the tables. Eventually, it would be this sense of investment that won him control over the sweetest mark he ever got, Cloud City on Bespin. After the Empire took her from him,

Down And Out On Coruscant

So much for Imperial unity. The way they threw themselves into the Mutiny, it made you realize they had been wanting to kill each other for decades — they had just been too busy killing everyone else to realize it.

That was what brought the Rebels to Coruscant. They'd been picking up some bad news from the Core. Apparently Imperial City was under attack — one faction of the Empire going after another. This could be a great opportunity for the Rebellion. It might be able to pick up some more info in the battle zone and maybe Lando and his crew could get something about the Deep Core codes they still hadn't gotten. Best of all, they could help stir up a zaproach nest while doing it.

Even Lando had no idea how bad things had gotten. When the *Liberator* emerged into realspace, it looked as if whole fleets had been destroyed. Next thing, three battlewagons start spitting out ident codes they'd never heard before. Lando supposed he'd been asking for it when he and Wedge decided a lone Star Destroyer would be less suspicious. Seconds later, the plasma starts flying hot and heavy; by they time they even saw the ion gun they were eating atmosphere. Luke somehow put the ship down with minimal casualties and they made the best of it.

They sent out teams to contact survivors, get info — the usual. Lando had done a fine job of keeping the troops together and getting them in a relatively safe spot. They'd had to face down Imperial troops, but at least they were able to avoid the heart of the battle. Meanwhile, Luke was following up on a very unpleasant rumor he'd heard.

They waited several days before a rescue team showed up. On the fifth day, their luck had finally given out. Some Imperials found the *Liberator's* crew and decided to engage in some target practice. With the Rebels only armed with hand blasters against AT-ATs, battle droids and TIE tanks, it wasn't much of a challenge. The only thing that saved them was Han Solo and Leia arriving with sorely needed backup. Coruscant was gone, but at least they got out.

he was a changed man — now he wasn't content to let luck be so fickle. If he wanted things to go for him, then he had to make them work out.

He'd sold out his friend Han to keep the cape on his back and saw how empty that was. Then he devoted himself to fighting the Empire as a payback. Once the chips were in the right hands, he could set up some new investments. Only he didn't know the game wasn't over yet.

Nkllon had been working out, both for him and the New Republic, only to be destroyed by the Empire. The Empire wasn't going to let him or anyone else make a decent profit as long as it was throwing its weight around. Of course, Lando still had cash here and there. It was time to use some of his profits to fight the Empire.

Ackbar, past differences or not, owed him some favors. He got his command back and the next thing he knew, he and Wedge were running those Imperial cruisers taken at Endor, the *Liberator* and the *Emancipator*. Soon they were running deep into Imperial space and helping to splinter the already fragile Imperial alliance. It was so easy — cruise up to an Imperial task force, use some pirated codes some "old friends" stole for him, and fake his way inside. Then, when the Rebel ships opened fire, they could leave "clues" that the attack was from one of the other Imperial factions.

Of course, this trick couldn't work all the time. That it was on a mission to Coruscant when the whole thing blew up in his face — what were the odds? As the *Liberator* plummeted down into the atmosphere, Luke took the controls and somehow put the thing down without killing everyone on board. Soon enough they got rescued — all of them save Luke. *Well,* Lando figured, *he's a grown up, and he's gotta know what he's doing.* Lando figured he could put in for some downtime when he got to Pinnacle.

En route, the word came down about the World Devastators attacking Calamari. He would never understand this fixation of the Empire's, but he knew a danger when he saw one. He and Wedge teamed up on the *Emancipator* to lead the Battle of Calamari; Lando and his crew did their part. Lando has been playing the role of general to the hilt: staff meetings, strategic briefings, the whole works. Responsibility, indeed. Well, it was just an investment in the future as he saw it. Especially with that promising deal in Colundra Sector …

■ General Lando Calrissian

Type: Gambler
DEXTERITY 3D+2
Blaster 9D, blaster: hold-out blaster 7D+2, brawling parry 6D+1, dodge 7D+1, grenade 5D, melee combat 5D+1, melee parry 5D+2, thrown weapons 4D, thrown weap-

THAT'S IT! INFORM PINNACLE BASE WE'RE IN POSITION OVER CALAMARI!

DEFLECTOR SHIELDS UP! PREPARE TO TAKE FURTHER OFFENSIVE ACTION!

ons: knives 6D
KNOWLEDGE 3D
Alien species 5D+1, bureaucracy 8D, bureaucracy: Imperial Navy procedures 9D+1, business 8D+1, business: mining 11D+2, business administration 8D, cultures 7D+1, languages 6D, planetary systems 5D+2, streetwise 9D, survival 6D+2, survival: urban 8D, tactics: capital ships 5D, tactics: starfighters 6D, value 7D, willpower 6D+1
MECHANICAL 2D+1
Archaic starship piloting 5D+1, astrogation 7D, communications 6D, ground vehicle operation 5D+1, hover vehicle operation 5D+1, repulsorlift operation 5D+2, sensors 5D+2, space transports 9D, starfighter piloting 9D, starship gunnery 8D, starship shields 8D+1, swoop operation 5D+1
PERCEPTION 4D
Bargain 9D, bargain: minerals 10D+2, bargain: tibanna gas 11D+2, command 8D+2, con 10D+1, forgery 7D, gambling 10D+1, hide 7D+2, persuasion 7D+1, search 5D, sneak 7D+2
STRENGTH 2D+2
Brawling 6D+2, climbing/jumping 5D+2, lifting 4D+2, stamina 6D+2, swimming 4D+2
TECHNICAL 2D+2
Computer programming/repair 5D+1, demolition 3D+1, droid programming 4D+1, droid repair 4D+1, first aid 4D+1, repulsorlift repair 5D+2, security 7D+1, space transports repair 8D, starship weapon repair 6D+2
Force Points: 3
Character Points: 21
Move: 10
Equipment: Comlink, hold-out blaster (3D+1 damage), sabacc card deck

R2-D2

Artoo-Detoo never thought that when this newest battle with the Empire started that he, a lowly astromech droid, would be the one being to stop the Empire's new secret weapons. Artoo takes the appreciation of his friends in stride, quietly proud in the knowledge that he contributed to the survival of the Rebellion, just as he did all those years ago on Tatooine and Yavin.

Artoo has seen enough combat in the last year to last him the rest of his days. From Thrawn's use of clone-piloted armadas to the Emperor's horrible World Devastators, it seemed that war never seemed to cease. It was as bad as the Clone Wars! His friends had not taken these battles well. Especially Master Luke.

That was not what worried him now. Luke had been acting very strangely, particularly around this Emperor. Luke had surrendered his lightsaber and promised to serve him. Artoo had seen other friends go over to the "Dark Side," as Luke seemed to be doing, but that didn't mean that he understood what was going on.

While on Byss, Luke allowed the Imperials to hook Artoo up to their computers. Luke eventually got him out of there, but not before those techs started clearing countless programs and files off his memory systems. In the process, those clumsy techs started disassembling Artoo's motivators and even burned out his

differential regulators. They probably were trying to erase his personality — and that was the kind of action Artoo took very personally.

Many Humans have their droid's memories erased every few months to "improve" the droids and prevent them from developing personalities and new programming. Luke and the others never did that, and Artoo appreciated it. While Master Luke had every right to have him reprogrammed, Artoo thought that he and Luke had a special understanding — that he was more like a friend than a servant.

Only after sizable chunks of information had been loaded did Artoo begin to understand. All this was so that he could store the Master Control Signal. The immense size of the file, and the programs that allowed him to manipulate the file, required a huge amount of Artoo's memory. The more Artoo thought about it, the more Artoo began to realize that Luke really hadn't entirely turned against his friends. The astromech droid quickly deduced that by loading these codes into his memory banks, he could give them to the Alliance and even control the machines himself! His Master had not betrayed the Alliance!

Of course, Luke was still acting strangely. He didn't understand why he stayed behind on Byss when Solo and the Princess left. Even now, Master Luke seems distanced from what is going on around him — as if he is deep in thought, computing some strange mathematical function. It must be the return of the Emperor that has so tormented his Master. Artoo knows that restoring his lost files is easy enough; if only Humans were as easy to fix.

■ R2-D2
Type: Industrial Automaton R2 Astromech Droid
DEXTERITY 2D
Electroshock prod 4D+2, dodge 5D
KNOWLEDGE 2D
Planetary systems 9D, survival 6D+2, value 7D+2
MECHANICAL 4D
Astrogation 12D, communications 7D, repulsorlift operation 6D+2, sensors 8D+1, starfighter piloting 7D, starfighter piloting: X-wing 9D, starship gunnery 5D, starship shields 5D+2
PERCEPTION 3D
Command 4D, con 4D+2, gambling 6D, search 4D, sneak 5D
STRENGTH 3D
Lifting 4D, swimming 3D+1
TECHNICAL 4D
Computer programming/repair 9D, droid programming 5D+2, droid repair 8D, machinery repair 5D+2, repulsorlift repair 5D, security 7D, starfighter repair 7D, starfighter repair: X-wing 9D+2, space transports repair 7D, space transports repair: YT-1300 transport 9D+1
Equipped With:
• Three wheeled legs (one retractable)
• Retractable heavy grasper arm (+1D to *lifting*)
• Retractable fine work grasper arm

- Extendable .3 meter long video sensor (360° rotation)
- Small electric arc welder (3D damage, .3 meter range)
- Small circular saw (4D damage, .3 meter range)
- Video display screen
- Holographic projector/recorder (one meter range)
- Fire extinguisher
- Small internal "cargo" area (20 cm by 8 cm)
- High pitch acoustic signaller
- One long range sensing array; includes radar, Geiger counter and life form sensor, infrared receptors, electromagnetic field receptors (add +3D to *search* at range of up to 100 meters)
- Broad-band antenna receiver (can monitor all broadcast and communication frequencies)
- Information storage/retrieval jack for computer link-up
- One compressed air launcher (used for Luke's lightsaber or for flares)

Force Points: 1
Character Points: 5
Move: 5
Size: .96 meters tall
Cost: Not for sale
Equipment: Long-range comlink attachment (100 kilometer range)

C-3PO

C-3PO often finds it ironic that he, a protocol droid programmed specifically for diplomatic functions, has become so indispensable in wartime. All he ever wanted was to pursue the fine points of etiquette and social discourse.

Instead, he seems to have bounced from mishap to mishap, none of it ever his fault. It's enough to make one's logic circuits short-circuit.

Once upon a time, a long time ago, he was privileged to serve the House of Alderaan. This was where 3P0 felt he belonged. He rather liked it there with the endless state dinners and masquerades and such. Of course that was what had gotten him in this mess to begin with. Part of the Organa family entourage, Threepio had attended the annual Emperor's Ball, where he met Darth Vader in person. He'd only been trying to make small talk, and certainly it wasn't his fault that he mistook the Lord of the Sith for a new model of GuardDroid. He was really only trying to pay a compliment, but 3P0 had been assigned to preschool duty for a year.

Then, he somehow ended up in the Labor Pool where he was paired with R2-D2, since astromech models speak only binary and need a translator. Threepio considers R2 to be his

--THANK THE MAKER! ARTOO -- I KNEW YOU COULD DO IT! YOU SAVED THE DAY!

BEEEEP-PWEEP-BOOP-BIP-BIP-WHREET-DOOT-VRR-FRADEET-BREE-DOOPVADEET-DRRP-TWEET-BRAZZZZ !!!

greatest friend, even though the little droid doesn't always know his place.

Threepio's misery, however, never ends. There is that horrible desert planet that Master Luke called home, where the past two times he visited he ended up suffering massive cosmetic injuries, not to mention the humiliation of serving as a translator for that loathsome Jabba the Hutt.

Of course, there was the encounter with the stormtroopers on Bespin and being reassembled by the Wookiee. He still didn't feel his neck axial pistons were up to snuff. And they let the Wookiee fly the ship sometimes …

And then there were those harrowing encounters on Honoghr with the Noghri and the Grand Admiral. And being rigged to impersonate Princess Leia by having his vocabulator modified. And, to top it all off, the constant insults from Captain Solo. Will it ever end?

From his files on the Corellian system, they had droids there, just like everywhere else. Odd that Captain Solo acted as if he didn't understand that Threepio was only looking out for everyone's welfare. Even now, after all they had been through, Solo still found new and interesting epithets for him. He must compile a study on it sometime. Now if they asked him his opinion, obviously Chewbacca was the brains of the pair, and ought to handle the business end too. Of course, Han was fouling the Organa bloodlines now.

These days, Threepio often serves as part of Princess Leia Organa's political entourage. When not involved with the princess, he is often working with the Republic staff in the cryptology department. At least decoding abstract codes or alien languages is more useful than running around the universe shooting people. Not that what a droid wanted seemed to matter that much. He couldn't see much point in shooting each other all the time. The World Devastators were intelligent after all (more so than the men who piloted them, most likely). In all the fighting, no one suggested talking to them to see how they felt about the whole matter. Of course you had to talk very slowly to Imperial machines anyway, but it might have made a difference.

After Master Luke returned from Byss, he had given 3P0 some files and datachips full of hieroglyphics to translate. He said it should remain between the two of them, but Threepio could guess from what Artoo said that it had to do with the Force. Master Luke seemed to be getting more and more obsessed with the Dark Side and while he didn't understand it all, it certainly worried him.

■ C-3PO

Type: Cybot Galactica 3P0 Human-Cyborg Relations Droid
DEXTERITY 2D
Dodge 5D+2
KNOWLEDGE 5D+2
Alien species 8D+1, bureaucracy 9D, cultures 8D, languages 13D, planetary systems 6D, survival 5D+2, value 5D+2
MECHANICAL 3D
Repulsorlift operation 5D+2, space transports 3D, starship shields 3D
PERCEPTION 3D+1
Bargain 7D, con 6D+1, hide 5D, sneak 5D
STRENGTH 2D
TECHNICAL 3D
First aid 4D
Equipped With:
• Humanoid body (two arms, two legs, head)
• Two visual and two audial sensors — Human range
• Broad-band antenna receiver
• AA-1 Verbo-brain
• TranLang III Communication module with over seven million languages
• Vocabulator speech/sound system capable of providing an extraordinarily wide range of sounds including sound effects and exact impersonation of Princess Leia's voice as well as very passable imitations of Han Solo, Chewbacca, Lando Calrissian and Luke Skywalker
Force Points: 1
Character Points: 2
Move: 8
Size: 1.67 meters tall
Cost: Not for sale

General Wedge Antilles

Wedge Antilles is in many ways a typical Corellian: independent, reliable and born with a passion for spaceflight. He has taken that passion and used it for the benefit of the galaxy. As a young fighter pilot for the Rebel Alliance, he helped in the Battle of Yavin. With a few more years of experience, he and Luke Skywalker helped forge Rogue Squadron, which has become the most famous and decorated fighter squadron in the Rebel Alliance. Now, he serves the Alliance as a general, and was a vital part of Alliance Command in the Battle of Calamari.

Besides his efforts at the Battle of Calamari, Wedge was instrumental in the New Republic's success at the Battle of Bilbringi. His ability to outguess the enemy and to lead his pilots to

victory earned him an outstanding commendation from Mon Mothma. He was also promoted to general, and given command of his own wing of fighters, which he renamed Rogue Wing.

In recent months, he helped coordinate the evacuation of Coruscant when the Empire retook it from the Republic, and commanded Rogue Squadron in several pivotal engagements. He also made notable contributions at the Battle of Sluis Van and the Battle of the *Katana* Fleet. Added to his list of commendations for the Battle of Yavin, the Battle of Hoth and the Battle of Endor, Wedge has had quite a career.

At first, Wedge was hesitant to accept this promotion, but he accepted a compromise he and Ackbar could live with. Wedge would accept the promotion to general and the duties of Fighter Command Liaison, but he would retain his flying rights and could lead Rogue Wing on missions. This way he can still do what he loves, flying, while avoiding being the oldest lieutenant in the Alliance.

One of Wedge's first assignments as a general was the series of surprise assaults on the Imperial System. Though these missions are, of necessity, in captured Star Destroyers, the New Republic has filled their hangar bays with the X-wings of Rogue Wing. Rogue Wing got off light — most of the ships were on the *Emancipator* when the *Liberator* was shot down. Of course, Wedge was with Lando and Luke when the *Liberator* crashlanded on Coruscant.

Once everyone evacuated from the *Liberator,* Wedge was amazed to see the damage to Imperial City. In the short years he had been stationed on Coruscant, he had come to know the gleaming towers and endless alleys, mazes and levels of the city. Much of the city was destroyed in the endless fighting. He wouldn't lay any odds about the Republic relocating there anytime soon.

After the stint in the Imperial City war zone, Wedge and Lando were directed to the Battle of Calamari. While Lando and General Madine tried to coordinate the ground forces, Wedge worked diligently with General Bel Iblis coordinating various aspects of the air defense. He also helped General Rieekan coordinate with General Dodonna at Alliance Command on the Pinnacle Moon.

■ General Wedge Antilles

Type: Brash Pilot
DEXTERITY 3D
Blaster 5D+2, brawling parry 4D+1, dodge 6D+1, melee combat 4D+1, melee parry 4D, vehicle blasters 4D
KNOWLEDGE 2D
Alien species 5D+2, bureaucracy 6D, cultures 3D+2, languages 4D+2, planetary systems 6D+2, streetwise 5D, survival 5D
MECHANICAL 4D
Astrogation 7D+2, repulsorlift operation 5D+2, space transports 5D+2, starfighter piloting: X-wing 7D+2, starship gunnery 7D+1, starship shields 6D
PERCEPTION 3D
Bargain 5D, command 6D+2, command: Rogue Wing 8D+2, gambling 5D, hide 4D, search 5D, sneak 4D
STRENGTH 3D
Brawling 4D, stamina 6D, swimming 5D
TECHNICAL 3D
Computer programming/repair 6D, repulsorlift repair 4D+1, space transports repair 6D, starfighter repair: X-wing 6D+2
Force Points: 1
Character Points: 11
Move: 10
Equipment: Blaster pistol (5D damage), comlink, blast vest (+1D physical, +1 energy), Rebel Alliance uniform, survival pack (see page 96 of *The Rebel Alliance Sourcebook*)

Zev Veers

Zevulon Veers was born to a life of power and prestige, but he sacrificed it all for what he believed in. Eldest born child of General Maximilian Veers, his mother died of a rare disease while on holiday. That summer was the last truly happy one he can remember of his childhood. Father was an up and coming Imperial officer with a good career ahead of him, but there was something nagging at young Zev's conscience. As he grew older, he grew increasingly distant from his father and missed the warmth of his mother's smile, although he went to the finest schools and wanted for nothing.

Except answers to questions that dogged him. Like why his tutors, who were obviously more intelligent than him in many ways, were slaves. Or why his father spoke endlessly of the "glory of power," yet never seemed to mention that the military's job was to serve and protect the citizens of the Empire. Or why friends of his father who spoke their minds on Imperial policy kept on disappearing. These led to other questions. Ones no one would give him an honest answer to. Whether his father couldn't or wouldn't answer these questions, they stayed with young Zev. It seemed that so much of what the Empire stood for was a lie. His father talked of glory and courage, but how much courage did it take to bomb planets from orbit? Or to enslave aliens?

When Zev had to join the local Sub-Adult Group (SAGroup) battalion, he was reluctant.

Wegsphere was enjoyable enough, but he didn't get along with the other kids very well. He liked the idea of working to improve society, but somehow marching in formation and climbing mountains while singing pro-New Order anthems didn't seem to be what he was looking for.

He managed to make it through the adolescent period without any big mistakes, but things changed when his father took him aside to discuss how the bad marks from the Political Reliability Observer might hurt the general's career. That really bothered him, the way his questions and apparently innocuous remarks about the slave camp field trip were betraying his father. Zev would keep his ideas to himself from then on.

He made it for his first few years after that with no repeats of his earlier mistakes. That didn't mean that he accepted the party line whole. His teachers had taught Zev too well. Courses in philosophy and logic only made the case against the New Order stronger. Media reports and propaganda broadcasts could only hide so much and Zev didn't like what he could read between the lines.

Junior officer training came and went, but not soon enough for Zev. His father was a hard man, and wanted his son to grow up that way too. Zev hoped his assignment would turn out be an army post. He knew better. His father wouldn't hear of his son taking a non-combat position. First, he had to survive his CompForce hitch. "CompFarce" was more like it. They weren't much better than teens carrying loaded weapons. He was getting tired of saluting, sprogstepping and singing hymns to the New Order.

It was here that Zev reached his breaking point. It was only a few short weeks after the Battle of Hoth and his father was the Empire's newest military hero. He had just returned from a short leave with his father, and Zev had been treated like a hero as well. By the side of his father, he went to endless celebrations and heard countless speeches about the glory of the Empire and how the Alliance was immoral and doomed to defeat.

After Zev returned from the glamour and ceremony, he learned what the Empire really stood for. During a routine police action, Zev was assigned to bodyguard the battalion commander while he interrogated prisoners. Intending to harden the young man to the sight of torture, the commander, Ivo Laibach, showed off his ISB training. Zev was horrified as the Rebel, an old man, was beaten mercilessly and tortured. Even the other two "CompFarcers," boys younger than he, started turning green.

Luckily for Zev, while the commander man-

GENERAL CALRISSIAN, WE'VE INTERCEPTED A NEW *HYPERSPACE COMMUNICATIONS CHANNEL* ... BEAMED BETWEEN *CALAMARI'S ORBIT* AND THE *GALACTIC CORE.*

THEY'RE TRANSMITTING IMAGES OF THE *DESTRUCTION* ON CALAMARI...

handled the local librarian, the real Rebels showed up. Laibach, idiot that he was, went outside "to take care of the nonsense" and got wounded by the Rebels for his trouble. It would be funny if it weren't all so horrible.

Zev came to a decision: he couldn't just let the old man die. So he untied the librarian and used a medpac on him — just as the librarian's daughter, the Rebel squad leader, came to his rescue. Initially she was distrustful of Zev, but she was won over by her father's testimony. Zev was still taken prisoner, but not treated much like one.

That was a few short months before the Battle of Endor, where the Empire faced defeat. In the six years since, Zev has become a full-fledged Rebel. He is now doing what he wants. He still hopes that someday his family will reject the Empire and that his father will understand, but he hasn't seen or heard from his father since he deserted the Empire.

When he occasionally is mistaken by some for Zev Senesca, a Rebel pilot who gave his life for the Rebellion, Veers is nonplussed — "I only hope I can be worthy of the comparison someday."

■■ Zev Veers

Type: Young Senatorial
DEXTERITY 3D
Blaster 5D, brawling parry 4D+2, dodge 5D, grenade 3D+2, melee combat 5D, melee parry 5D+1
KNOWLEDGE 4D
Bureaucracy 4D+2, cultures 4D, planetary systems 5D, value 5D, willpower 4D+2
MECHANICAL 2D+2
Astrogation 3D, beast riding 4D+2, capital ship gunnery 6D, capital ship piloting 5D, repulsorlift operation 3D+2, starship gunnery 5D+1
PERCEPTION 3D+1
Command 3D+2, search 4D+2
STRENGTH 3D
Brawling 4D, climbing/jumping 4D+2, lifting 4D+1, stamina 4D
TECHNICAL 2D

Computer programming 5D, demolition 3D+2, droid repair 5D, first aid 3D+2, security 5D+1
Character Points: 8
Move: 10
Equipment: Helmet comlink, blaster pistol (4D damage), blast helmet (+1D physical, +1 energy), blast vest (+1D physical, +1 energy)

Kane Griggs

If you asked Kane Griggs why he joined the Rebel Alliance, he might give you a dozen reasons. However, he won't mention the biggest reason of all — Marfa Thorbin.

Griggs grew up in the Botor Enclave on a frozen planet called Kerensik. Winter was the only season he had ever known until he came to the university. Most of the students who took political studies in Imperial schools were hoping for cushy jobs in the bureaucracy, Griggs included.

There was a Civil War going on, but that didn't concern him much. The whole conflict was all a million light years away. He supposed he objected to some New Order policies on an abstract level, but he was more interested in becoming an economist. He was a student in his first year, his first time off-world as well, when he met her.

Winter was approaching, but for now they had something called "autumn." He rather liked it — so much color, and even the plants had leaves that turned colors as well. He first met her while coming back from a lecture. He had, of course, seen her somewhere before, probably in one of his classes, but he couldn't tell since so much was a blur with exams coming on.

He was walking, counting the leaves, when he ran into her. Picking up each other's books they began chatting. By way of apology, he offered to buy her a cup of *chav*. Initially embarrassed at his clumsiness, he was surprised to find she too was counting the leaves. She said she had grown up on a different world and was used to all sorts of weather. Everything about her was different from what he was used to.

She wanted to be an aquatic xenologist and someday explore ocean worlds. When they parted, he made a mental note to look for her in his classes. Happily, she was in two of them and the pair began an easy friendship as study partners. Eventually, winter vacation came and they promised to communicate. They corresponded frequently enough, but he was still surprised when she transmitted a hologram of leaves from her world. He was amazed at the rich greens, so unlike the spines Kerensiki trees had.

When they met again during the spring semester, they could revel in the coming season. Even over another summer break, there was something about Marfa that he couldn't forget. Finally, after years of friendship becoming love, he decided he would ask her to marry him. She accepted and they set a date, but first she wanted to go home to bring the good news to her parents on Alderaan.

She was but one of the Death Star's victims. When the New Republic claimed victory at Endor, he quit his job in the Botor Income Ministry and joined up as a recruit. Some doubted his usefulness aboard a warship, but he wouldn't listen. In service to the New Republic he has found a new life filled with friends, happiness, and even a wife and child. These days he doesn't think of Marfa much. But he knows why he fights.

■ Kane Griggs

Type: Rebel Navigator
DEXTERITY 2D+1
Blaster 5D+1, brawling parry 3D, dodge 5D, vehicle blasters 4D+2
KNOWLEDGE 3D
Alien species 4D, bureaucracy 6D, economics 7D, planetary systems 5D+1, survival 5D, value 5D
MECHANICAL 3D+2
Astrogation 7D, capital ship gunnery 4D+2, capital ship piloting 6D+2, capital ship shields 5D, communications 7D, repulsorlift operation 5D+2
PERCEPTION 2D+1
Bargain 5D, con 4D, hide 5D, search 4D, sneak 4D+2
STRENGTH 2D+2
Brawling 4D, climbing/jumping 4D, stamina 5D, swimming 3D+1
TECHNICAL 4D
Capital ship repair 6D+2, computer programming/repair 6D, droid programming 5D+1, droid repair 6D, repulsorlift repair 5D+2, security 6D
Character Points: 6
Move: 10
Equipment: Comlink, Rebel uniform, blast vest (+1D physical, +1 energy), blast helmet (+1D physical, +1 energy), hold-out blaster (3D+2 damage)

Huoba Neva

Huoba Neva had her work cut out for her when she went to the Academy. Sullustan and female, she had two strikes against her in the pro-Human, male-dominated hierarchy of the Empire and its Academies. Still, Sullust was an important world to the Empire. Some compared their status to the Mon Calamari in the Rebel Alliance. Daughter of an Executive Board Member of SoroSuub, she was easily able to qualify for the Academy. If any had what it took, she did.

Neva was a perfectionist and she had always been good at team games and sports. A career in the military was the kind of challenge she needed to see how good she was. Someday she would apply that drive to the company. She cherished its support, but didn't want any favors; she wanted to succeed or fail on her own merits.

Upon arrival at the Academy, she threw herself into studies with the same aggressiveness

her family put into their business enterprises. She majored in command school and weapons systems, finishing fourth in her class. Soon she was an officer, some said the token non-Human, but her skill spoke for itself.

Neva had a good career in the Navy, but it was not good enough. She wanted a command. Not some transport, but a scout ship or other combat vessel where she could make a name for herself. She bided her time when less talented officers got the good assignments. She set her sights lower and lower, hoping even for command of a lowly mining tug rather than a career of being an undistinguished officer.

After three years without a promotion, her patience wore thin. Her record was spotless and even her political reliability was good enough — she knew what she was up against. Sullustan society felt that if you wanted something, you worked for it, and if you worked hard enough, you got it. This didn't seem to be the case with the Empire. If this was true for her, mightn't it be true for her species? For other species as well? SoroSuub did fabulously well, but the big break into the ranks of the megacorporations, like the ones in the Corporate Sector, never seemed to come.

It took her a while to come around to the idea of joining the Rebel Alliance. She was no anarchist, and politics was something she gave lip service to just to get by. Being a soldier was what she did best, and if the Empire wouldn't give her a challenge, then the Rebellion would. She came over to the Alliance at the height of the fighting, a strong statement for one so ingrained in the ways of the SoroSuub Corporation, which was still staunchly pro-Imperial.

Ackbar in particular had heard a good appraisal of her from Sian Tevv, a prominent Sullustan diplomat and a political agitator who was leading the fight for SoroSuub and the Sullustan people to join the Rebel Alliance. Tevv had watched her career and when he saw her dissatisfaction he told his aides to act. They made the appropriate offers and, burning her bridges behind her, she defected. Now Sullust is a proud Republic world thanks to Sian Tevv, and Neva was the youngest Sullustan warship captain in the Republic Navy.

She still pushed herself hard. It wasn't enough to get a command — she needed to prove she *earned* it. The commendations she got after smashing the Imperial-backed insurgency in the Illoud system made it worth it all. She then was promoted to command of the escort frigate *Rebel Star,* which was destroyed off Coruscant while on the mission to rescue the crew of the *Liberator.* Neva's brilliant career ended on that rescue mission, but her example will be an inspiration to her fellow Sullustans for years to come.

■ Huoba Neva

Type: Sullustan Navy Commander
DEXTERITY 3D
Blaster 5D, blaster artillery 4D+1, dodge 5D, melee combat 6D, melee parry 5D
KNOWLEDGE 2D+2
Alien species 6D, bureaucracy 5D, cultures 4D+1, planetary systems 6D+1, tactics: fleets 5D
MECHANICAL 4D+1
Astrogation 5D+2, capital ship gunnery 5D+2, capital ship piloting 7D+1, capital ship shields 5D, space transports 5D, starship gunnery 6D, starship shields 5D+2
PERCEPTION 3D
Bargain 6D, command 7D, command: Rebel Star 9D+2, con 5D+2, gambling 4D+1
STRENGTH 2D+2
Climbing/jumping 5D, lifting 4D+1, stamina 5D+2, swimming 5D
TECHNICAL 2D+1
Computer programming/repair 4D+2, droid programming 4D+1, security 6D
Special Abilities:
Enhanced Senses: +2D to *search* and *Perception* in low-light conditions.
Location Sense: +1D to *astrogation* when jumping to a location the Sullustan has visited before. A Sullustan can always remember how to get back to someplace she has visited.
Character Points: 8
Move: 10
Equipment: Comlink, Rebel Alliance uniform, hold-out blaster (3D+2 damage), holocrystal of her family

Syub Snunb

The Sullustans as a whole may have joined the Alliance rather late in the war, but once they did, they really devoted themselves to the task at hand. Syub Snunb is no exception to this. He had heard about Huoba Neva and Nien Nunb and the others who joined the Alliance. Still he didn't feel it was good to go against the wishes of his people.

Then came the day when the leaders began to talk about the wisdom of maintaining loyalty to the Empire. There had been talk of this sort for years, but the conservative minds at SoroSuub had always made it clear that their loyalty was to the Empire. These new rumors seemed to have more substance and the implied, but unspoken, voice of SoroSuub behind them. If SoroSuub finally gave credence to the old rumors about exploitation, colonialism and the other complaints, then there must be something to it all.

None of these worried Syub Snunb, however. He was a high ranking officer in the Sullustan home guard. Their planets, unlike most others, had the cities buried in warrens and tunnels. While they had orbital observation satellite ar-

rays, as any other high tech world did, for some reason pirates and criminal elements felt they could sneak into orbital space with impunity. So the Sullustans had to arrange a permanent system navy to protect their shipping and colonies. They realized that it would be better for public relations if the defense forces were Sullustan in origin. At the direction of SoroSuub, who benefitted the most from this anyway, a fleet of old cruisers and corvettes was assembled and the Home Guard was created.

Initially, they had to hire their own merchant spacers to crew the ships. Soon they had enough trained individuals to create a full time force. One of the first of these soldiers was Syub Snunb. He had been security chief for a line of cargo barges, and it was only natural enough for him to try his hand at full time combat patrols. He showed a real talent for it and soon worked his way up the ranks to where he was next in line to the Home Guard Commodore himself. He liked the responsibility and the sense of satisfaction derived from a job well done.

Then the Sullustan leaders finally put the matter of secession to a vote and to the amazement of some, it passed. Snunb was selected as the commander to lead the Rebel Command Fleet to the Sullust system, where the Rebellion's entire war fleet would assemble in preparation for the assault in Endor system. Rendezvousing at Obica, the Rebels checked him out thoroughly. He wasn't a firebrand by any stretch of the imagination, but he was a conscientious leader and a concerned captain. Satisfied it wasn't a trap, they followed him to Sullust.

It was with great surprise that he was chosen to be captain of one of their own ships, the escort frigate *Antares Six*. It was their way of showing good faith. Snunb had to admit he liked the sense of trust these Rebels radiated. As the years have passed, *Antares Six* has established a fine reputation for being one of the tightest run ships in the Republic fleet, and that's just the way Snunb likes it.

■ Syub Snunb

Type: Sullustan Captain
DEXTERITY 3D
Blaster 5D+1, blaster artillery 4D+1, dodge 4D, missile weapons 6D+2
KNOWLEDGE 2D+2
Alien species 5D+1, bureaucracy 6D, cultures 4D+1, law enforcement: Sullust law 6D+2, planetary systems 6D
MECHANICAL 4D+1
Astrogation 5D+2, capital ship gunnery 6D, capital ship piloting 6D+2, capital ship shields 5D, communications 5D, sensors 5D+2, space transports 6D, starfighter piloting 5D+1, starship gunnery 6D, starship shields 5D
PERCEPTION 3D
Command 5D, gambling 4D+1, investigation 4D+2, search 5D

STRENGTH 2D+2
TECHNICAL 2D+1
Computer programming/repair 4D+2, droid programming 4D+1, security 7D
Special Abilities:
Enhanced Senses: +2D to *search* and *Perception* in low-light conditions.
Location Sense: +1D to *astrogation* when jumping to a location the Sullustan has visited before. A Sullustan can always remember how to get back to someplace he has visited.
Character Points: 3
Move: 11
Equipment: Comlink, Rebel Alliance uniform with Sullust Home Guard patch on shoulder, hold-out blaster (3D+2 damage)

Mon Mothma

Mon Mothma hasn't much combat experience, but she is as much a fighter as any commodore or commando. The only difference is the battlefield she commands is one of diplomacy and etiquette. As a leading Senator, she fought the rise of Palpatine with every tool at her command. At the time, she was unaware that Palpatine used the Dark Side of the Force to sway the less conscientious Senators. Had she known, she still thinks she might have been able to make a difference.

That's in the past now. The time had come when she knew that all the proper and legal and even justified actions weren't ever going to stop his ruthless rise to power. Mon Mothma then had to take a pause and reconsider her options. After all, she had a responsibility to her constituents, but more importantly, she had a responsibility to the ideals of the Republic, which was crumbling around her. Given this situation, she reached a watershed moment when it dawned on her that force, equal in power but ethically applied, was the only solution.

Using her networks of influence, favors, patrons and followers, she began reaching out to other discontented groups. She finally made contact with groups of the Army and Navy of the Republic who had refused to submit to Palpatine's will. Uniting them with other groups, like the Atrivis Resistance Groups, she laid the groundwork for the Alliance to Restore the Republic. While she would have loved to leave the responsibility there with the soldiers and tend to her daughter's needs, it turned out that few of the generals or admirals had the political acumen it took to cement the

Alliance together.

Over the years, she would occasionally allow herself to take a tiny bit of pride in her accomplishments. Even with the death of Palpatine at Endor, many resisted the notion that the old ways were still applicable in a civilization that had grown used to autocracy. But she persisted in structuring the New Republic along the lines of the old. She truly believed the galaxy would revert to its natural course. She couldn't have been more wrong.

Only her daughter, convalescing on New Alderaan, sees behind the confident surface that everyone else is used to, sees how much the years have cost her mother. She can also see new resolve there as well. Realizing just how much her past policies may have cost the New Republic, Mon Mothma is now rethinking her priorities and assumptions. She is determined to avoid the mistakes of the past; it is time to revive the Republic and truly bring freedom to the galaxy.

■ Mon Mothma

Type: Chief Councilor
DEXTERITY 3D
Blaster 3D+1*, dodge 4D+1*
KNOWLEDGE 4D
Alien species 9D+1, bureaucracy 12D, bureaucracy: New Republic Provisional Council 13D+2, cultures 11D, intimidation 7D, languages 8D, planetary systems 9D, survival 7D, value 6D, willpower 8D
MECHANICAL 3D
Astrogation 5D, beast riding 3D+2, communications 5D+2, repulsorlift operation 4D+1, space transports 4D, starfighter piloting 4D
PERCEPTION 4D
Bargain 11D, command 10D, command: New Republic bureaucrats 10D+1, command: New Republic soldiers 11D+1, con 9D, gambling 6D, hide 6D+2, persuasion 8D, persuasion: debate 10D+1, persuasion: oration 11D, search 7D, sneak 4D+2
STRENGTH 2D
Stamina 4D*, swimming 3D*
TECHNICAL 2D
Computer programming/repair 6D, droid programming 5D, droid repair 4D, first aid 7D, security 5D+1, starfighter repair 2D+1
Force Points: 4
Character Points: 12

Move: 8*
Equipment: Comlink, datapad
* **Note:** Some skills have been lowered to reflect aging and lack of use.

Speech bubble: I HAVE ASSIGNED TEAMS TO ANALYZE *ALL* OUR POSSIBLE RESPONSES. WE'LL MEET AGAIN TOMORROW. I WANT YOU ALL RESTED--AND *READY TO ACT!*

General Jan Dodonna

Jan Dodonna, the mastermind of the Yavin victory, has become something of an elder statesman in the New Republic. Having lived through Old Republic, Empire and New Republic, he has participated in more battles and sieges than probably any other officer in the Alliance. In his day, Dodonna was as important to the Old Republic's navy as Adar Tallon, and he revolutionized siege warfare.

Still, the years of constant warfare and strategic planning have taken their toll on him both physically and mentally. At an age when most Imperial counterparts would be writing their memoirs, Dodonna still plans the New Republic's strategies.

Realizing that he could no longer make the full-time commitment that Mon Mothma and her staff required, he formed an impromptu body of advisors, including such retired notables as Adar Tallon, Pashna Starkiller and Vanden Willard (they jokingly call themselves the "gray cadre"). This group advises New Republic military commanders on areas of vital importance and in times of crisis. While none of them have the desire to serve full time (after all, it is time to make way for a new generation of officers), their invaluable experience is most welcome in situations where each decision could decide the course of a battle. Following Endor, Dodonna had already gone into semi-retirement on New Alderaan, but when even he was surprised at how much life was left in the Empire, he came back to advise Mon Mothma and the Inner Council.

The Battle of Calamari and the return of the Emperor was where the gray cadre shone. Their advice helped the Alliance formulate some of its most successful combat tactics in the battle, and their decisions helped save millions of civilian lives during the siege of the Calamari homeworld. Not only that, Dodonna had formulated a plan with recalcitrant Bothans, supervising their attempt to steal the master control code of the World Devastators. If Luke had failed to get those control codes to the Alliance, Dodonna's plan would have been the only hope for victory against the World Devastators.

Now that the battle is over, these men will return to the more relaxed combination of retirement and strategic planning. While not devoting themselves full-time to these tasks, they gather monthly as a strategic think tank, analyzing the long term goals and plans of the Empire. If

--HE WILL LAUNCH A SERIES OF *WAVE ASSAULTS* UPON ALL WORLDS IN PROXIMITY TO THE GALACTIC CORE...

MOVING OUT FROM THE CENTER, HE WILL NOT REST UNTIL THE *ENTIRE* GALAXY FALLS UNDER THE SWAY OF THE *DARK SIDE!*

ever activated again, these advisors will be instantly ready to provide information, analysis and military planning to the military leaders like Ackbar, who run the day to day fighting.

Dodonna is more than ready to turn over the reins to younger warriors, like Madine or Antilles. They now have the kind of experience they need to carry the torch. Of course, should they ever need advice or a friendly word of encouragement, he and the others will be there to give it to them.

■ General Jan Dodonna

Type: New Republic General
DEXTERITY 1D+2*
Blaster 3D*, dodge 3D*, melee combat 3D+1*
KNOWLEDGE 3D
Alien species 6D, bureaucracy 6D, cultures 7D+1, languages 9D, military history 7D+2, military history: modern fleet battles 12D+2, planetary systems 8D+1, tactics: capital ships 9D+2, tactics: fleets 7D, tactics: sieges 10D+2, tactics: starfighters 7D+2
MECHANICAL 3D+2
Astrogation 5D+2, repulsorlift operation 6D, space transports 4D+2, starship gunnery 4D+2
PERCEPTION 3D+1
Bargain 5D+1, command 8D+2, con 9D, gambling 9D+2, search 7D, sneak 5D
STRENGTH 1D+2*
TECHNICAL 3D
Computer programming/repair 7D, demolition 5D, droid programming 7D, droid repair 5D+2, security 7D+1
Force Points: 2
Character Points: 15
Move: 8*
Equipment: Datapad, blaster pistol (4D damage), comlink
* Note: Some attributes and skills have been lowered to reflect aging and lack of use.

General Crix Madine

Some say the reason so many Corellians turn to smuggling is because they don't have the talent for anything else. Of course, no one ever says that in front of a Corellian. Despite the fame of the Corellian smugglers, the vast majority of Corellians, like any other people, are hard working folks going about their business and trying to live their lives in a crazy, sometimes brutal and dangerous universe. Crix Madine isn't a smuggler; he is disciplined, orderly and responsible, and one of the best generals the Alliance has ever had.

He had gained a bit of a reputation as a martinet among his troops in the Imperial Army. That was because he refused to let one's CompForce connections or wealth or family status affect his evaluation and treatment of his soldiers. Madine thought it

better to work them half to death on the parade ground than let them go into the field untrained; half dead is remarkably better than being completely dead. This may have rankled his political officers, but the results he got stifled any serious reprimands.

Madine had a fine, even admirable record in the Empire: very few casualties, no conspicuous defeats, and what gave him his greatest pride, no atrocities ever committed by his troops. Not that that was exactly an Imperial priority; quite the contrary. Still, in an organization that all too often settled for rule by fear, he liked to win the "ideas and sentiments" of those he dealt with. That was what ultimately drove him to defect to the Rebellion — the one person he couldn't convince about the Empire was himself.

So he found a way to let his old friend Rieekan put in a good word for him when he got there. He erased his files and disappeared. When he arrived at Alliance Headquarters, he found it working overtime. After Endor, which he'd helped plan out, and even after years of countless defeats for the Empire, they had never let up. When Sluis Van was attacked, he knew his suspicions were right. The whole mess at Calamari was only the topping. Madine is not exactly anxious, but he is all too aware that the decisions he and the staff make in the next few years may determine if the history books record him as one who helped restore freedom, or as another "traitor" executed by the Empire.

■ General Crix Madine

Type: New Republic General
DEXTERITY 2D+2
Blaster 6D+2, blaster artillery 5D+2, blaster artillery: anti-infantry 9D, blaster artillery: anti-vehicle 7D+2, brawling parry 5D, dodge 7D+1, grenade 5D+2, melee combat 5D, melee combat: force pike 7D, melee parry 4D
KNOWLEDGE 3D
Alien species 6D+1, bureaucracy 6D+2, languages 4D+2, military history 12D, planetary systems 7D, streetwise 5D, survival 5D, tactics: ground assault 10D+2, tactics: squads 14D, willpower 5D+2
MECHANICAL 3D+2
Beast riding 5D+2, beast riding: Cracian thumper 6D+2, capital ship gunnery 4D+2, ground vehicle operation 5D+2, powersuit operation 5D, repulsorlift operation 6D, starship gunnery 5D

PERCEPTION 3D+1
Bargain 5D+1, command 10D+2, con 5D+1, gambling 4D+2, hide 6D+1, persuasion 5D, search 7D, sneak 6D+1, sneak: forest 6D+2
STRENGTH 2D+1
Brawling 6D, climbing/jumping 4D+1, stamina 6D+1, swimming 3D+1
TECHNICAL 3D
Computer programming/repair 5D, demolition 6D, droid repair 4D+2, first aid 4D+1, ground vehicle repair 4D+2, security 7D+2, space transports repair 6D, starfighter repair 4D+2
Force Points: 1
Character Points: 12
Move: 10
Equipment: Blaster pistol (4D damage), comlink, datapad

Rebel Sea Commandos

The New Republic, much like the Alliance in its day, and the Old Republic before that, controlled a huge amount of space. Even in these days of decline, the Republic still controls an immense amount of territory. In that territory there are millions of worlds, all of them unique. Essential to maintaining control over these worlds and defending them from attack is the ability to adapt to the local environment, no matter how exotic.

Most life-bearing planets have large amounts of water on their surface; sometimes a majority of the surface is water. This presents problems to military action since there is no effective cover and the turbulence can throw off the best aim. In many ways, water is an extremely hostile combat environment. The Old Republic had equipment to allow some actions in marine environments, but without the proper skills and training, the usefulness of these items was marginal.

The Alliance's answer to the unique challenges of naval engagements are the Rebel Sea Commandos. This group is trained exclusively for the challenges of surface and subsurface water combat.

It is the Empire that can indirectly take credit for initiating the Rebel Sea Commando training program. Several years ago, the Empire was researching a possible gravity well generator in the Sedri system. The soldiers in this operation made use of specially designed equipment al-

lowing them to function at all depths. Since then, the Empire has maintained a small cadre of seatroopers, but their abilities pale before those of the Sedrians themselves.

When Rebels first landed on this world, it was the Sedrians who aided them and gave them valuable experience in the art of aquatic warfare. This allowed them to sneak aboard the Imperial garrison base and examine the Imperial equipment and compare it with their own. Based on this and some discussion with the Sedrians, the Sea Commandos took form.

Trained in all manner of water environments, Sea Commandos are shipped from one world to another to broaden their experience. One week, they might be on a swamp planet moving through opaque bogs and bayous; another week, they might be scrambling up waterfalls and cataracts. Another week might find them involved in ocean terrain. The training results in soldiers that the Republic can turn to for any duty in aquatic environment.

■ Rebel Sea Commandos: Average Soldier

Type: Rebel Sea Commando
DEXTERITY 3D
Blaster 5D+2, dodge 5D, melee combat 6D, melee parry 4D+1, missile weapons 5D
KNOWLEDGE 2D
Planetary systems 4D, survival: aquatic 5D, willpower 6D
MECHANICAL 4D
Beast riding 5D, communications 5D, repulsorlift operation 6D
PERCEPTION 3D
Command 5D, con 6D, search 5D+1, sneak 6D
STRENGTH 3D
Brawling 4D, climbing/jumping 6D+2, lifting 4D, swimming 7D, stamina 5D
TECHNICAL 3D
Blaster repair 5D, computer programming/repair 4D, demolition 6D, security 5D+1
Character Points: Varies, typically 0-8
Move: 10
Equipment: Blaster rifle (5D damage), 3 concussion grenades (5D damage), 3 stun grenades (7D stun damage), grapple gun (uses *missile weapons*, three magnetic grapples with 100 meter cable), blast helmet (+1D+2 physical, +2 energy), blast armor (+2D physical, +1D energy), waterproof uniform, survival kit (see page 96 of the *Rebel Alliance Sourcebook)*, military headset comlink

Chapter Two
The Empire Reborn

Overview

The Old Republic had endured for millennia, evolving and maturing till it was as familiar as the night sky itself. Misty tales surrounded its birth and cloaked the heroes of its early years in the grandeur of legend. But as the Republic grew complacent, corruption flourished. Weakened thus, the Republic fell prey to the ambitions of one man and collapsed, a ruthless Galactic Empire rising in its place.

The Empire was founded by Palpatine and the members of his corrupt councils. Seeing the spirit of malaise omnipresent about him, he formulated his "New Order." He gained the support of several small ideological and parliamentary cliques and rallied them around his noble-sounding propaganda. This led to the formation of a movement called the Commission for the Preservation of the New Order (COMPNOR).

What no one could know was just how strong the unassuming president's ties to the Dark Side were. He knew only the Jedi Knights could defeat him, and so he took steps to eliminate them. Palpatine held absolute power through fear and violence. Compared to the Republic, the New Order was in its infancy, having endured only a few decades. But in that time its hold over the lives of its citizenry had become so invasive, its control so absolute, that those who fought against it seemed almost mad to rebel at all.

Around the New Order was gathered all the power a galaxy could offer: military might, in the form of star fleets; secret police, formed from the remnants of the Republic's Intelligence services; and, an elite body of advisers and Dark Side Adepts.

The Defeat at Endor

During the difficult weeks immediately following the debacle at Endor, the problem was all too apparent to the Imperials themselves. In an absolutist state, power must be wielded abso-

(The following are textfiles on holo-posters placed in public areas in the Empire.)
Citizens:
Do not be fooled. You have heard accusations from REBELS. Accusations of "atrocities," of war crimes. They create these to deceive you.

These are lies. Why would they lie to you unless they were desperate, unable to achieve victory?

THE EMPIRE IS VICTORIOUS ON ALL FRONTS!

REBELS?
The only ATROCITIES are theirs, as they destroy order and peace.
They began this WAR.
They are TERRORISTS.
They are CRIMINALS.
They are MURDERERS.
Trust your leaders. We defend you from those who would replace the New Order with anarchy and economic misery.
Support Your Empire.

THE EMPIRE IS VICTORIOUS ON ALL FRONTS!

SUPPORT THE EMPIRE.
Enlist in the military, donate goods, inform on suspects — today!
Don't suspect them. INFORM ON THEM!

THE EMPIRE IS VICTORIOUS ON ALL FRONTS!

lutely. But by whom? It became increasingly apparent that succession to the throne was something the Emperor, so circumspect in everything else, had never seriously prepared for. When the Emperor was killed during the Battle of Endor, the speed with which the Empire's structure disintegrated amazed even some Alliance strategists. Obviously something was going very wrong in the Empire.

Some felt an unwitting heir might prove better than no heir at all, so a genealogical trace was proposed. Unfortunately, nearly all of Palpatine's personal records had been deleted from the known libraries. Nor had the Emperor left a will or any final orders.

During these chaotic months, the one person who might have offered some clue to a resolution was Grand Vizier Pestage. As Steward of the Imperial Personal Archives, he was privy to Palpatine's most secret holo-communications and recordings — if an heir was to be found in the Emperor's correspondence, this was where to look. Pestage refused, providing no explanation.

Many feared Pestage might have his eye on the throne. He had been running many of the day-to-day affairs of the Empire on his own even before the Battle of Hoth, allowing the Emperor to go about his arcane studies. To some minds, it seemed quite likely he might claim some executive privilege.

The ranks of Imperial Advisors, never cooperative in the best of times, felt a new kinship and closed ranks against Pestage. Within weeks, he was impeached as Vizier, formally censured, and stripped of his properties, titles and privileges. All that saved him from the disintegration booth was his surprising offer to retire permanently to private life on Byss, the Emperor's personal sanctuary world. Little did anyone suspect his real reasons for doing this.

If the Emperor had not left a designated successor, and there was no constitutional procedure for one, then those with ambition felt they must make a new emperor from among themselves. But the Empire seemed uncontrolled and uncontrollable. Charismatic leaders who seemed capable of asserting power were toppled by jealous rivals and their own greed as time and the Alliance fleet trampled the once great Empire.

This crisis in authority was now seriously harming the war against the New Republic, and public confidence was eroding rapidly. Of course, the rule in the individual sectors had not changed significantly in the inner portions of the galaxy, but as Mon Cal cruisers, Corellian Corvettes and the rest of the Republic fleet drove Star Destroyers from planet after planet, there was a growing sense that the "Imperial juggernaut" would face defeat. Soon, when many spoke of Palpatine, it was as *an* emperor, no longer as *the* Emperor. Sheer arrogance led them to blame Palpatine for the failings of the Empire, rather than look to their own weaknesses and folly.

It proved nearly impossible to coordinate the hundreds of surviving task forces across the sea of space. Access codes changed overnight, troops received inconsistent orders, and commanders were intractable and independent. The Navy might order a system under Rebel siege defended, only to find a few weeks later the same fleet had been, with all proper procedure, redirected to an insignificant fortress world deep in the Core.

Furthermore, each planet to join the New Republic was one less world to pay taxes into the once limitless treasury, causing one fiscal crisis after another. This wasn't helped much by the fact that Palpatine had always kept the left hand guessing what the right was up to, so any attempt to streamline the enormous spending programs proved futile. All attempts to guarantee proper apportionment of credits vital to perimeter defense efforts failed. Huge sums continued to be spent on useless projects, like the long delayed palace in the Corporate Sector.

Most notable was the ceaseless construction on the prototype *Eclipse*-class Super Star Destroyer. Designed as a flagship for the late Emperor, it was typical of the type of self-aggrandizing acts that had once been obsequiously approved, yet couldn't now be justified. Clearly, naval planners felt traditional ships of the line were what were needed to handle the Rebellion, not some grandiose yacht sitting for years in space dock with no sign of completion.

The Empire disintegrated under its own weight, splintering into countless independent factions with cautious allegiances to other factions, and all swearing loyalty to the "Empire." All this time, while party officials, admirals and advisors jockeyed for some clear mandate, the New Republic was more than ready to fill the vacuum. Of course, they had their work cut out for them: strategically the Empire was dying like a wounded vornskr, but just like a vornskr, *that* was when it was most dangerous.

With so much chaos, it was unsurprising that dozens of systems opted out of either side and formed independent system-states. Neither Empire nor Republic could spare the personnel or the resources to make much of an appeal to these iconoclasts. Both sides resolved to settle the more important matter of which government would survive first, and then parley with these worlds.

Ironically, many turned to nostalgia for the Old Republic as a solution. Despite his dissolution of the Senate, Palpatine had been elected by that body in the first place, so many tried to claim its backing. Former senators were drafted, cajoled or bribed into becoming figureheads, supporting this Moff or that general in their ambitions.

The Republic steadily forced the Empire back, claiming system after system, sector after sector. Some Imperial factions fought to the death, such as those under Lord Shadowspawn; others surrendered and were absorbed into the growing Republic.

Others proposed peace plans. For example, three years after Endor, Admiral Betl Oxtroe began making secret overtures to members of the New Republic to negotiate the creation of a parliamentary monarchy. She proposed Ederlathh Pallopides, an eleven year old remote grandniece of Palpatine, as heir. The Republic's Provisional Council would replace the Imperial Advisors in exchange for amnesty for the military. Sadly, the first round of talks had only begun when the Admiral fell to an assassin's blade, presumably wielded by Noghri, and the plan was forgotten.

Four years after Endor, the New Republic controlled half the galaxy and was able to claim Coruscant, once the capital of the Empire.

The Coming of Thrawn

Five years had passed since Endor, and the strains were threatening to tear the Empire apart, when from the outlying regions of the galaxy came a series of ident codes. Unquestionably authentic, they accompanied a holo message from the last surviving Grand Admiral, named Thrawn. The squabbling ministers knew just how important a Grand Admiral could be to reverse the tide of defeat. Even the most myopic of them knew how empty rule would be without an Empire to rule over.

Putting aside their differences for the time being, they managed to arrive at a consensus: a war hero such as Thrawn might be exactly what they needed. As a non-Human, he was a complete outsider with no power base save his own competence. He could rely on no support other than what they chose to give him. Such a situation could prove advantageous, if he could accomplish all he claimed. If he could destroy the New Republic, they might make him their figurehead Emperor, with their power behind him. And if he eventually proved too independent for them, he could always be eliminated.

For half a year, Imperial supporters allowed themselves to remember the "glories" of the past. Thrawn was Emperor in all but name. While Thrawn's fleet was but a small portion of the Empire's once unimaginably vast war fleet, and Thrawn's support was far from universal or even enthusiastic, he had managed to bring the New Republic to its knees, even blockading Coruscant with a deviously simple siege weapon. Imagine, then, the ministers' disappointment when, after so promising a start, he ultimately perished. True, he had won back much of their lost territory, but the job was still unfinished.

After Thrawn's defeat, the remaining fleet commanders joined with the Ruling Circle and within days had recaptured vital Imperial systems. But they still weren't satisfied: although bloodied, the New Republic still controlled much territory. The ministers, munitions tycoons and functionaries turned immediately back to their plotting. Only now, there was more to be won.

The Mutiny

Now that the final victory over the Alliance seemed inevitable, the factions of the Empire tried to establish a government. The Old Republic had endured many calamities, and yet survived them all. Until the collapse of order that spawned the Empire itself, the Republic had survived for millennia against disasters, plagues, wars and betrayals. Surely the Empire could shake off its lethargy and restructure itself to suit the coming times.

As time passed, it became apparent this change was not forthcoming. This was because, during the era of the Old Republic, most of those in the government were dedicated to serving their constituents. Many were highly motivated and brought intelligence and honor to their duties. Even during the worst crisis of the Republic, there had been a sense of the great traditions and idealism that had forged it from the sprawling diversity of the galaxy.

Not so with the Empire. Unlike the Republic, it had not been created to bring justice and prosperity to all. Rather, it was the striving of a single individual to imprint the galaxy with his own mark. Now that mark was fading and it was up to his followers to find the will to survive the disaster of his passing.

Not to say all who served the Empire were corrupt or cynical or depraved. There were many, many misguided souls who genuinely felt the Empire could restore the Old Republic's glory and sought to create what they called a "New Order with a Personal Face." They were never at the heart of power; they lacked the predatory instinct that was necessary to achieve real power in the Empire.

Suspicious to the point of paranoia, the Emperor had always scrupulously avoided any delegation of power. Major decisions made by ministers or advisors had to be personally ratified by his chosen servants, usually Grand Vizier Sate Pestage. He allowed, even cultivated, the rivalries of his ministers, warriors and bureaucrats.

What none had dared speak in more than a whisper in years past was now a topic of open debate among the ruling bodies of the Empire. The most important officials in the government, Imperial Advisors like Ars Dangor, blithely suggested the new ruler be selected from their ranks by election. All the Advisors would convene in the old Senate building on Coruscant and, in secret negotiation, would select a ruler

and crown him. They would then sit in as a legislative body, overseeing the new ruler's decisions.

The Moffs and Grand Moffs, front line governors of the realm, approved … with a single caveat: they must be allowed to join the convocation. They further suggested participants get a number of votes equal to the number of worlds they controlled. Realizing this would stack the odds in favor of the governors, the advisors politely demurred.

None of this sat well with the COMPNOR leadership. Wealthy party functionaries and corrupt officials, they were out for themselves as much as anyone, and exploited the fervor of their supporters. These followers were CompForce chiefs and other New Order purists in the government. As far as the "true believers"

STILL DEFENDING THEIR FLOATING CITIES AGAINST IMPOSSIBLE ODDS, THE VALIANT *MON CALAMARI* EXULT AT THE SUDDEN REBEL ONSLAUGHT!

ADMIRAL ACKBAR HAS NOT ABANDONED US! HE'S CALLED DOWN THE *WHOLE ALLIANCE* ON THEIR HEADS!

were concerned, the Empire *was* the New Order, and to make any decision based on political convenience was nothing short of treasonous. They demanded litmus tests of ideological purity.

Most intransigent of them all were the officers of the Inquisitorius. Charged with rooting out all that smacked of the old ways during the Great Purge, they had long since outlived any usefulness. Though a new Grand Inquisitor hadn't been appointed since Lord Torbin died in an accident on Weerden, they were unaware of their unpopularity. They felt persecuted by COMPNOR, military and advisors' operatives, believing them secretly beholden to Rebel interests. They resented the independence of the military and staged show trial after show trial to cow resistance.

Meanwhile, the navy and army had quite different opinions. It had always been they who had maintained the Empire, by force when necessary, so who better to rule than those who controlled that power? Realizing how useless a direct claim to the throne would seem with the war still raging, they appointed themselves kingmaker, even if they had to turn the power at their command against their fellows.

Grand Admiral Thrawn's huge success was limited to retaking territory, not uniting the Empire itself. Instead of reuniting the disparate elements of the Empire, the unfinished victory only served to push them farther apart. With victory almost within reach, the stakes were suddenly that much higher and the potential for bloodshed had risen proportionately. The navy demanded the right to pick a new Grand Admiral from the chain of command and continue as planned. Of course, the army demanded a say in the matter as well.

In response, the bureaucracy claimed the warlord's defeat invalidated this claim and had crippled the offensive. With regional armies and CompForces at their disposal, they felt confident enough to rattle their weapons.

Finally, after months of political maneuvering, the standoff ended. The inevitable occurred, as tensions escalated and violence exploded. The remnants of the Empire were now engaged in a full-scale civil war. No one is sure how or why, but fleets bombarded rival worlds from orbit, destroying whole planets. Unlike the attacks by the New Republic, which avoided wholesale destruction of property and lives, no such mercy was granted by Imperials.

What side you supported even determined what the conflict was called, much as the war against the Empire had gone by many names: "Rebellion" to the rulers, the "Galactic Civil War" to the insurgents. Most outsiders called this conflict "The Imperial Civil War." COMPNOR/ISB purists called it "The War of Purification," while those opposing the militarists began calling it "The Mutiny." Most just referred to it as the "Time of Destruction."

Perhaps the most intriguing aspect was the role played by those who still maintained a link to the Dark Side. Though the opportunity existed, none of them made any sort of claim on power. Most believed the supporters of the Dark Side dead or sufficiently discredited, and most of the contenders preferred it that way.

Since the Emperor had given his two major secret police agencies overlapping authority, they fought constantly. Imperial Security Bureau (ISB) and the Ubiqtorate of Imperial Intelligence even assassinated each other's operatives on a regular basis. Now, with full-scale war raging, their tenuous truce collapsed. Imperial Intelligence published proscription lists naming "enemies." Partisans were offered incentives to betray and assassinate their fellows, and by doing so gain possession of their property. Initially very successful, this method of operation was duplicated by ISB, and eventually by others as the sides splintered further.

Seeing a window of opportunity, the New Republic pressed its advantage to the fullest, sending its captured Star Destroyers to stir up even more trouble. But no one, not the numerous pretenders to the throne nor the Republic's leaders, could see that the Mutiny was not an accident. It was being allowed to happen, all involved manipulated by some unseen and unknown player.

The Heir to the Emperor

To a degree unseen since the days of Xim the Despot, Palpatine had created a state that simply couldn't function without him. It was no accident that the Empire was collapsing around his grave. No one could doubt his fondest wish had been that, if he should fall, then the universe would burn on his funeral pyre. And burn it would after Darth Vader, Lord of the Sith, hurled its master to his doom.

During the height of the Mutiny, signs began to appear of a purpose behind the confusion. The Grand Vizier wasn't acting out of some notion of tradition when he preserved the integrity of the Emperor's Archives. He was simply following his master's commands. It was quite kind of the advisors to allow him to retire to Byss. To him, time could solve all mysteries and crises. He already knew that a true heir to the Empire had indeed arrived.

It was the original emperor, Palpatine himself.

To be sure, there had always been "fanatics" who claimed the Emperor would one day return, but few paid them any heed. No one in their wildest nightmares thought Palpatine had survived. But he had — still weakened from this metamorphosis, the Emperor would do nothing to regain control. He was still too vulnerable to take command back, but as the years passed and one pretender after another rose and fell, he grew stronger and angrier.

While it was imprudent to reveal his return, he could still hinder or aid those who caught his fancy. It was, in fact, the Emperor who had given all the various orders and counter-orders that were impeding the petty plans of the various factions. Here then was the reason so many of the warships Thrawn needed had vanished into the fortress systems, forcing him to rely on the *Katana* fleet of lost Dreadnaughts. It was the Emperor, also, who ordered that the construction of new palaces and his flagship continue. All in preparation for the day when he would announce himself to the galaxy and take his throne back. But first, more time to heal, then the destruction of the revolutionaries who had caused him so much trouble.

Palpatine knew precisely why the Empire couldn't last without his dread power: he had designed it that way. No one ever suspected how much he relied on the Dark Side of the Force. He shaped those of his government by using the Force against them. He used it to control his fleets and to drive his soldiers on to victory. He used it to destroy his enemies from a distance and learn of conspiracies against him. Without it, there was no way the Empire could endure, as he had designed it. The Dark Side flowed through him like some primordial ichor and was the key to all his power. It was the key to his destiny: for the Dark Side, coupled with his mastery of cloning, was the key to immortality.

Soon he was ready to strike. Fully healed and in greater control of the Dark Side than ever, he finally acted to end the Mutiny. In the past, he had been content to let his "children" tear each other to shreds. Such destruction would cull out the weak, the cowardly, the stupid. Now that he was truly indestructible, he could afford to set his standards higher.

None of those struggling to seize power ever realized they were being observed from the audience chambers on Byss. All things were weighed and considered by the Emperor. Spies moved everywhere with confidence, probing loyalty, checking for those most likely to prove worthy. Then, when the time was right, they were brought before him. Depending upon the person's reaction, the Emperor either rewarded their loyalty with a place in his new Empire or extinguished their lives. The incompetent and the recalcitrant were executed and their battalions decimated in the ancient, barbaric tradition, as a sign of his new, merciless posture. If, by dying, they would make the survivors better servants, then so be it. There would always be throngs to replace them.

The Final Design

As the time approached when he would venture forth against his enemies, Palpatine marshalled his legions together. In orbit about his world of Byss, all things fell into place.

Palpatine chose Calamari as the first of the major Republic homeworlds to die. And so his fleet moved. Once Calamari was totally and publicly "cleansed," the fleet would move out and destroy other worlds until final victory was achieved. First, however, the Calamari who had so publicly defied him in the past needed to be eliminated from the galaxy, thereby teaching all those who would oppose him a lesson.

Let his enemies doubt or scoff. The revivified Emperor would be prepared for them all. Nothing would be left to inferiors this time. While an advance force would launch the initial attack on Calamari, the final assault would be led personally from his newly completed flagship. Equipped with all the weapons of a dozen lesser craft, he would be invincible in battle.

The Emperor's proudest creations were the World Devastators, which were his choices to begin the punishment of Calamari. Unlike the Death Star, which merely destroyed planets, these machines consumed the metals, carbons and rare elements locked in a planet's core and used them to manufacture new and more powerful fighters, attack craft and weaponry. As each world fell, its resources would be used to fuel the assaults on other worlds.

Most important of all, however, was the plan the Emperor had contrived to destroy his enemies. Called the "Shadow Hand Strategy," it was a summation of the Emperor's battle philosophy. This time, his forces, purged of all the willful and ignorant, would act in unison to sweep all resistance away. The plan was an autopilot system for the Empire itself.

Palpatine realized the Empire couldn't hope to emerge victorious without its designer at the helm, but it could avoid the wholesale destruction it had just emerged from. One such Civil War was useful to prune the nest of vipers — but a second would not be necessary or wise.

Ominously, this plan provided the Dark Side Adepts with a secret and chilling role to play.

While his closest advisors remained ignorant, each did have access to as much of the plan as necessary, and knew it was in their best interests to follow it precisely. In the wake of Palpatine's destruction at Pinnacle Base, it remains to be seen just how effectively his plans will be carried out.

Emperor Palpatine

Palpatine paused in his study on Byss, holding the Jedi Holocron aloft in his hand. A mere trinket, a brief glimpse of the limitless power of the Force. He considered his next move. It was almost time to make himself known again ...

Palpatine was a very patient man — even his harshest critics had to admit this. Just how patient most of them could never guess. Such patience came with his long study of the Force, and it was to the Dark Side that he owed his allegiance. For the Dark Side was power. Power to shape the galaxy, to change history, perhaps to live forever.

His death he had planned for, just as he had planned for every other contingency. Still, this last time had been quite different from all the others. Previously, the clones had been only meters away and the passing voluntary, in the comfort of his chambers. Nothing like the time of betrayal by his Dark servant. This time was so abrupt and unexpected ... so unpleasant that it felt as if, perhaps, a part of his being had been left in space over Endor.

He had spent over a year disembodied, formless, drifting through the maddening void of the Dark Side. He had never foreseen having to transport his spirit so far across space. He had nearly dispersed forever, but he had survived, and now need never fear death again.

As soon as consciousness flickered back to a new clone body on Byss, he opened his eyes. All was as he had planned. He laughed out loud. He had won! The Rebellion had defeated his fleet, but he would return to rule the galaxy again.

He knew there would be war among his servants since none of them had the knowledge or power he held. But he wasn't in a position to act just yet. Years of rest and recovery lay ahead. Perhaps it was better this way. His forces had failed him, and the price for failure was what it had always been, death.

As years passed and he grew stronger, he began to concentrate more on his Dark Side studies. Still, he did grow occasionally concerned when one leader or another would come close to silencing the others and claiming the throne. Such ones were dealt with easily. He could let any of his Dark Side Adepts or other loyal servants handle the matter. After all, he still had his Hands and his Noghri.

When his servant, Thrawn, made his claim, Palpatine could only watch in sadness. He had hoped Thrawn would know better. It was heartening to see how effectively Thrawn dealt with the cruel hand fate had dealt him. A lesser person would have despaired. But a lesser person would have never been chosen as a Grand Admiral by Palpatine in the first place.

Still, no contender could ever be allowed to become too powerful. It was no accident when Thrawn fell. Palpatine never knew if Thrawn guessed that he was being used to divert attention from his own return.

C'baoth was a more curious case. Thrawn was brilliant enough to realize only an *insane* Dark Jedi would violate the Emperor's ban ordering them all into silence years ago. While they waited in their castles for their Emperor's command, Thrawn had sought out the one who would have forgotten all such orders years ago. It was most satisfying to watch the mad Jedi's mind unravel.

And, then there were Mara Jade and the Noghri. They would all have to be punished for their treason ... in time.

When both Thrawn and C'baoth were slain, he knew it was time to announce his return. Rather than reveal himself all at once, though, he chose to let the game continue at a lesser pitch. Only those who proved competent and loyal to his vision would be spared. Summoned individually under innocuous pretenses, each of the leaders in the Mutiny were brought to the audience chamber. Their reaction in that moment determined whether they would live or die. Once convinced of their commitment to his name, they were released and given their new orders.

More important than any admiral or weapons system, Palpatine had his grand design. First considered as he waited for the Alliance fleet to walk into his trap over Endor, it was the culmination of all his plotting. This battle plan made use of all his resources — not simply COMPNOR or the military, but everything. This even included his Dark Side Adepts and Dark Jedi.

As his plan moved into action and the World Devastators decimated Calamari, Palpatine activated one of the key ingredients of this Shadow Hand Strategy: a new servant to replace Vader. Soon, he had corrupted the son of Skywalker and tamed him. Little did the boy realize that his pathetic attempt at betrayal was already known by Palpatine. Known and provided for, as the opportunity to destroy Palpatine was the bait to lure Luke into plunging into the Dark Side's embrace forever.

As soon as Skywalker's dream of conquering the Darkness from within was crushed, the next stage in his training began. Fully under Palpatine's power, the boy would make a worthy disciple, as would his sister and her children in time. Perhaps he would enter the new unborn life and regain real flesh, but he would need preparation first. With the knowledge gained from his Dark Side Compendium, he would create an eternal dynasty, with the descendants of Skywalker as its nobility, and Palpatine himself as its omnipotent ruler.

As his plan proceeded, he became convinced that there was nothing between him and the eternal rule of Darkness. Even Ulic Qel-Droma would be envious of Palpatine. He had succeeded where all others had failed in taming the

Dark Side. He would journey across the universe spreading the shadow of his rule, blotting out the stars themselves, and taking his Dark Rule to other helpless galaxies.

Now, though, there was only the maddening darkness, caused by the betrayal of the Skywalker bloodline again. This charade would have to be ended …

Note: The following statistics are for the Emperor as he is depicted in *Dark Empire*. His Force skills have increased significantly in the six years since he was last seen in *Return of the Jedi*.

The Emperor appears in three unique physical forms in this series, but he has the same skills. The first version is his clone body at its physical peak, youthful and powerful, when he has been reborn in *Dark Empire*, comparable to his early days in the Senate. Version two is his mature form, where he is at his physical peak and corresponds to the final battle of *Dark Empire*. The ancient Emperor of version three is the one depicted in *Return of the Jedi*, and in the Emperor's first appearance in *Dark Empire*.

Part of the inherently corrupt nature of Palpatine's life force causes his new clone bodies to decay at a greatly accelerated rate. As his bodies age, he finds himself having to expend greater numbers of Force Points and Character Points to avoid having his body consumed by his own corruption.

■ Emperor Palpatine

Type: Jedi Master
DEXTERITY 2D+1
Blaster 8D+1, brawling parry 8D, dodge 10D, lightsaber 13D, melee combat 9D+2, melee parry 9D+1, running 7D
KNOWLEDGE 4D+1
Alien species 10D+2, bureaucracy: Empire 14D, cultures 9D, intimidation 14D, languages 9D, law enforcement: Empire 8D, military history 14D, planetary systems 7D+1, scholar: archaic library systems 10D, scholar: arcane technologies 12D+2, scholar: clone vat systems 7D+2, scholar: Dark Side Lore 15D+1, scholar: Jedi lore 14D, scholar: lightsaber histories 14D, survival 7D, tactics: fleets 12D, tactics: ground assault 6D, value 10D+1, willpower 13D

MECHANICAL 2D
PERCEPTION 4D+1
Bargain 10D, command 11D, command: Imperial Forces 13D, con 8D, hide 7D+1, investigation 8D+2, persuasion 13D, persuasion: oration 15D+2, search 8D
STRENGTH 3D
Brawling 8D, climbing/jumping 7D+1, lifting 7D, stamina 9D, swimming 5D
TECHNICAL 2D
Computer programming/repair 5D, droid programming 4D, lightsaber repair 10D, first aid 5D, security 8D
Special Abilities:
Force Skills: Control 15D+2, sense 17D, alter 15D+1
(Palpatine has spent decades studying the most arcane and esoteric Jedi disciplines. It is believed that he has mastered nearly all the known powers, previously unknown powers, and devises new ones at his pleasure)
Control: Absorb/dissipate energy, accelerate healing, control pain, detoxify poison*, enhance attribute*, hibernation trance, rage, reduce injury, remain conscious, resist stun, short-term memory enhancement*
Sense: Combat sense*, danger sense*, instinctive astrogation**, life detection, life sense, magnify senses, receptive telepathy, sense Force, sense path**
Alter: Injure/kill, telekinesis
Control and Sense: Farseeing*, lightsaber combat, projective telepathy
Control and Alter: Accelerate another's healing, control another's pain*, feed on Dark Side**, Force lightning*, inflict pain*, return another to consciousness, transfer Force
Control, Sense and Alter: Affect mind, control minds, create Force storms, doppleganger, drain life essence, enhanced coordination*, telekinetic kill*, transfer life
Sense and Alter: Dim other's senses
This character is Force-sensitive.
Force Points: 40
Dark Side Points: 50
Character Points: 85
Move: 11
Equipment: Lightsaber (5D damage)
* This power is described in the *Dark Force Rising Sourcebook.*
** This power is described in *Galaxy Guide 9: Fragments from the Rim.*

Commander Titus Klev

Titus Klev was always one of the lucky ones. His father was a highly placed officer during the Clone Wars and had married into a wealthy merchant family on Alsakan. When Klev was born, he wanted for nothing. He was among the first children to enroll in the newly formed Sub-Adult Group regiment formed on his world. There, he began the life of a model New Order citizen, the first generation to be raised entirely under the influence of the Empire.

Bright, athletic and good looking, many already thought he had what it took to go far in the Empire. Sure, his SAGroup activities weren't always popular at school when they included informing on "disloyal" educators in school or harassing alien children. However, nobody could object to him taking first place in the mock combat games and making first string on the Wegsphere team.

At the age of 13, on the recommendation of his SAGroup neighborhood warden, he was selected to attend special motivational camp on Ibanjji. There he survived the harsh conditions, and when he saved an instructor from a wild pack of varns, he got approval to join CompForce even though he was four years under the standard age.

Though he volunteered for Assault, a few words from his parents got him transferred to Observation duty on a customs ship. Nothing much happened (to his parent's considerable relief), and he finally worked his way up to Chief Ideological Monitor. Still, he craved some excitement and eventually chose the Naval Academy. While his grades weren't good enough to make officer training his first year, a fellow SAGroup member on the Admission staff bent some rules. Soon, he could boast of being the 37th generation of Klevs accepted.

While some worried he might spend more time at Wegsphere than studying, he took his responsibilities seriously. His contacts with the Campus COMPNOR Cadre didn't hurt, either. He was the kind of healthy, wholesome Human the propaganda branch loved to feature in media puff pieces, and he soon graduated at the top of his class.

Assigned to Battle Station Operations, it seemed for a while like his fabled good fortune might have run out. The second Death Star was destroyed before it could be completed and Titus never got to serve aboard it, so he spent his tour on a number of nameless Dedicated Siege Platforms and orbital bases, achieving no glory.

With the Alliance suddenly in the ascension, it seemed a bad time to be an Imperial officer, but Klev knew his opportunity would come. And come it did during the Siege of Wann Tsir. Quite by accident, he caught a Rebel agent sabotaging the shields. This earned him the right kind of attention.

Quickly rising through the ranks of Battle Station Command, Klev was popularly perceived to be on a fast track to a Moff position. So it was with considerable pride that he accepted his first command, the World Devastator *Silencer-7,* the lead ship in an assault force made up of the Empire's newest weapons. Their target: Calamari. He figured his luck was holding, but he was wrong. Klev became but one of countless fatalities when Artoo Detoo's Master Control Signal command ordered the *Silencer-7* to attack the other World Devastators, resulting in the annihilation of the entire fleet of fearsome vessels.

■ Titus Klev

Type: Imperial World Devastator Commander
DEXTERITY 3D+2
Blaster 4D, dodge 5D
KNOWLEDGE 3D+1
Bureaucracy 4D+2, planetary systems 4D, survival 6D, tactics: siege weapons 6D+2, tactics: World Devastators 8D+1
MECHANICAL 3D
Astrogation 5D+2, capital ship gunnery 5D+2, capital ship shields 5D, World Devastator operation 6D, starship gunnery 4D+1
PERCEPTION 2D+2
Command 6D, command: *Silencer-7* crew 9D+2, search 5D+1
STRENGTH 2D+1
Stamina 4D
TECHNICAL 3D
Computer programming/repair 4D+1, droid programming 6D+2, security 5D
Force Points: 1
Character Points: 11
Move: 10
Equipment: Comlink, blaster pistol (4D damage), Imperial Commander's uniform, rank cylinder

Deppo

Raised on the factory world of Eriadu, Grand Moff Tarkin's own Sector capital, Deppo showed a lot of spunk when growing up, but not much motivation. All he liked to do was tinker with swoop engines and go skyscraping along the spires and smokestacks of his heavily polluted planet. Eventually, he fell in with a gang of joysmashers who would hotwire the speeders of the wealthy, ride around in them, and then smash into barriers and energy pylons for laughs.

Thrown out by his parents at 11, he made money stripping wrecks for parts and selling them to dealers, as well as using them to repair vehicles and resell them on his own. Things went well till he got caught stealing a hoverbike owned by bodyguards of Governor Tarkin's niece. More competent and less vicious than many Imperial guards, they only stunned young Deppo. Instead of dooming him to slavery in JuveCourt, they gave him a job as a junior tech in the Moff's motor pool.

Here he was in paradise: he could tune and recalibrate the sophisticated military vehicles to his heart's content. After years of hard work, they sponsored him for engineering school on his twentieth birthday. Here he was trained for an eventual position aboard starships as an engineer. He was shown all the secrets of power outlay differentiators and the differences between alluvial versus artesiatic dampeners in coupling motivators, among other things.

With the skills he gained there, he could have named his price in the private sector, but he knew that his place was in the Empire. He wasn't concerned about the ethics of the vehicles he was working on — he only cared about the machinery. All that mattered to Deppo was that he wanted to fix the best, and only the Empire made the best.

His high marks earned him a post with a Walker battalion stationed on Nyasko in Colunda Sector. Because Colunda had a strong Rebel presence, he had his work cut out for him repairing sabotaged and battle-damaged wrecks.

Eventually, he was transferred to Admiral Comeg's fleet in the Core, where he was given the chance of a lifetime — calibration engineer aboard a new prototype Imperial siege engine, called a World Devastator. Deppo wouldn't just be fixing drive plates; here he would be supervising the automated factories which could mass produce attack craft from scratch. In conjunction with the assembly commander, he would be responsible for maintaining the high rate of production needed in battle.

Deppo is typical of the all-important class of technicians in the Imperial military. He was so wrapped up in his job that he never stopped to think about the innocent civilians on the receiving end of "his" war machine. Of course, that is exactly the mindset that got him into so much trouble.

As Calamari Defense Force troops penetrated the factory levels, he panicked. Fleeing to an escape pod, he jettisoned before the Devastator crashed. He was alive, but he was also floating towards the Calamari city that was under attack. When a Rebel Amphibion hailed him, Deppo had no choice but to surrender, and as a result, remains a Calamari prisoner of war.

■ Deppo

Type: Imperial Tech
DEXTERITY 2D+1
Brawling parry 3D+2, dodge 5D, melee combat 3D, melee parry 3D+2
KNOWLEDGE 4D
Bureaucracy 4D+2, planetary systems 5D, streetwise 6D+2, value 7D
MECHANICAL 2D+2
Repulsorlift operation 3D+1, starship shields 4D, World Devastator factory operation 5D+2
PERCEPTION 2D+1
Bargain 5D+1, con 5D+1, gambling 3D+2, hide 4D, search 4D, sneak 3D+2
STRENGTH 2D+2

Brawling 3D+1, stamina 4D
TECHNICAL 4D
Capital ship engineering (A) 6D, capital ship repair 10D, capital ship weapon engineering (A) 5D, capital ship weapon repair 7D+2, computer programming/repair 7D+1, droid programming 7D+2, droid repair 6D,+2, repulsorlift engineering (A) 8D, repulsorlift repair 9D+1, security 5D, starfighter repair 6D+2, World Devastator factory engineering (A) 9D, World Devastator factory programming (A) 9D+2
Character Points: 5
Move: 10
Equipment: Tech sealed suit (+1D physical, +2 energy), breather unit, monofusion welder (6D damage, uses *melee combat* skill in combat, Difficult difficulty), various tools and clips, datapad with remote link into central computer

Sate Pestage

When Imperial officers receive the command to make contact with the Emperor, as Darth Vader did during the Hoth campaign, one does not find him waiting at the other end. On the contrary, even the highest ranking official may spend hours waiting on bended knee for their master's pleasure. Often, he never responds at all. Of course, this never prevents any of his servants from making all haste to call anyway.

It is at this time that most of the elite of the New Order come to hate the Vizier the most. A wizened figure, with his hatchet face and scarecrow body jabbing out of his jeweled cassock, Sate Pestage performs the odious task of communicating his lord's wishes while the Emperor is busy.

Considering how infrequently he makes any public appearances, most assume this is his only duty. They couldn't be more mistaken, for the Grand Vizier is nothing less than the personal assistant to the Emperor in all things. Personally responsible for the preparation and tasting of the Emperor's meals, manager of his household, holder of the Imperial Seal, and chief scheduler of all functions, he determines who, of all those who request his master's attention, finally gain access. He is always scurrying about behind the scenes, obtaining some obscure datachip or arcane textfile, with only the soft whisper of his robes marking his coming and going.

Pestage has been serving the Emperor for decades now and shows no sign of letting up yet. It is not known how he first came to his service, but some suspect he may have been one of the first clones produced by the Emperor during his early rise to power. Others claim he is Palpatine's son by some forgotten wedding of convenience, who has aged normally while the Emperor constantly rejuvenated himself. What is known is that he speaks for the Emperor in all things and is tireless both in his loyalty and dedication to the Emperor.

■ Sate Pestage

Type: Imperial Advisor
DEXTERITY 2D
Dodge 4D
KNOWLEDGE 3D
Alien species 7D, bureaucracy 11D, cultures 9D+1, cultures: galactic etiquette 12D+1, intimidation 8D+1, languages 8D, planetary systems 8D, scholar: Imperial history 10D+1, scholar: Republic history 8D+2
MECHANICAL 1D+1
Beast riding 5D, repulsorlift operation 3D
PERCEPTION 2D
Bargain 7D, command 8D, hide 6D+1, investigation 9D+2, search 4D
STRENGTH 2D
Swimming 3D
TECHNICAL 1D+2
Computer programming/repair 7D+1, first aid 7D+2, security 8D
Force Points: 3
Dark Side Points: 4
Character Points: 11
Move: 10
Equipment: Ornamental datapad, robes, Imperial seal, personal force field (+5D for a 1 meter radius around his body)

Imperial Dungeoneers

The Empire, like any police state, has a huge number of "criminals" to deal with. Whether in slave labor camps, garrison stockades or dungeon transport ships, there is a need for specially trained and equipped troops to handle these inmates. Thus, the Imperial dungeoneers.

Depending on the security level of the prison, there are two types of armor they are issued. In low threat, minimum security situations, they are given light versions of army trooper gear, including chest piece, helmet and shoulder gear. Weapons include stunner pistols and glop grenades.

In more threatening circumstances, they are equipped with a complete suit of body armor. The helmet of this armor has an internal comlink (much like stormtrooper helmets), but these communication signals also carry life function information and continuously broadcast an audio and video record of what the Dungeoneer sees. The helmet is also equipped with a motion sensor with a range of up to 10 meters, giving the Dungeoneer a much greater chance of detecting potential threats before an attack is made. Through the comlink, a Dungeoneer can immediately sound an alarm in the case of a jailbreak.

Imperial Dungeoneers are armed with regular blasters or riot guns. Slave camp guards also carry buzz-knucks, power swords or stun batons.

Both armor types feature a unique buckle feature on the armor fasteners. It requires an electronic key that is kept in the guard barracks. This prevents prisoners from stripping the armor off and disguising themselves as guards.

Most Imperial prisons use knockout or nerve gases as a failsafe feature, so light-duty troopers carry breath filters; heavy security troopers have self-contained, independent air supplies. A pack of two dozen wristbinders is stored on the utility belt. Neuronic whips are occasionally available to work gang overseers as well.

Very few people have seen an Imperial Dungeoneer, as their presence is reserved for the most sensitive and dangerous prisoner handling actions. However, the Mutiny has caused some Dungeoneers to be reassigned to border patrol and military assignments.

■ Imperial Dungeoneers

Type: Imperial Dungeoneer

DEXTERITY 3D

Blaster 5D, brawling parry 4D, dodge 5D, melee combat 7D+2, melee parry 4D+1

KNOWLEDGE 2D

Intimidation 6D+2, law enforcement 5D

MECHANICAL 4D

Beast riding 4D+1, repulsorlift operation 6D

PERCEPTION 3D

Command 6D+2, con 3D, search 4D+1, sneak 4D

STRENGTH 3D

Brawling 4D, climbing/jumping 4D+2, lifting 4D, stamina 4D

TECHNICAL 3D

Computer programming/repair 4D, demolition 6D, first aid 4D+2, security 5D+1

Character Points: Varies, typically 0-5

Move: 10

Equipment: Dungeoneer armor (light duty: +1D to all attacks), Dungeoneer armor (heavy duty: +3D to physical, +2D to energy), blaster rifle (5D damage), stunner pistol (5D stun damage), glop grenade (3-meter blast radius, holds all targets with a *Strength* of 6D), buzz-knuck (STR+1D damage, 6D stun damage), power sword (STR+3D damage), neuronic whip (STR+1D damage, 4D damage (stun or normal) for five rounds), 24 wristbinders, stun baton (STR+1D damage, 5D stun damage)

■ Chapter Three
The Fringe

Overview

Anything for a Credit

The galaxy is a big place; sometimes things that might seem to be immense to a person might only affect a small portion of the galaxy. While whole sectors may undergo upheaval and chaos, others may experience golden ages of prosperity and abundance.

While the continuing civil war has unquestionably had a huge impact on society, it should come as no surprise that, for a large segment of the population, life goes on as usual. Most people are simply trying to make a living during a very difficult time.

Of course, there are others who are benefitting from the conflict. Some people call them the non-aligned forces; others call them the fringe; others call them the disinterested. It has been said that galactic civilization may rise and fall, and kingdoms may come and go, but there will always be people trying to make a fast buck. Welcome to the fringe.

The economics of the fringe are different from that of most other economic blocs of the galaxy. Under the Empire, the military corporations made fortunes, while the quality of life for the average person suffered. Much of the regular economy stagnated under the burden of unfair taxes and martial law. The wealthy have gotten wealthier at the expense of the regular citizens. Some are laborers who drone their lives away in hive-like factory complexes, under horrible conditions, making the tools of death, which are just as often turned against them if they dare to protest their treatment. Others are local farmers who, under "agri-sector maximization" policies, have been made into virtual serfs for macro-farming giants like the Tagge Restaurant Association, Core Foodstuffs and the Imperial Fruit Company. Of course, there were many hundreds of worlds still enjoying relative prosperity, but that prosperity is based on the exploitation of slave labor.

Now, with the war still going on, the economy

is even more unstable. Corporations go bankrupt or make fortunes on a regular basis. Other companies default on their loans and use military force to dissuade creditors. The value of the myriad of currencies in the galaxy fluctuates more rapidly than financial market computers can calculate. And, in between all this, are the members of the fringe, who are making and losing fortunes in the unethical pursuit of wealth.

Whatever the particulars, the current day is a bad one for nearly everyone trying to make an honest living. Ironically, the Empire, which campaigned on promises to restore order and law to outlaw regions and unite the disaffected, has caused the increase of crime. As dozens of smaller companies are swallowed whole by larger combines and the unemployment rate rises, many find no alternative but to join the Invisible Market or smuggle contraband.

The criminal organizations of the galaxy themselves have undergone much turmoil in the past few years. The death of Jabba the Hutt triggered a full-scale Hutt clan war, as Jabba had been the key player in establishing the truce that had lasted for many years. As the Hutts tried to systematically dominate each other, the galactic underworld plunged into chaos. New crime families sprung up and previously small, local crime operators like Talon Karrde found themselves building massive empires in a few short years.

Grim as this all sounds, there is cause for hope. As the New Republic gains strength, there is more opportunity created every day. One of the most crucial segments of the economy is the ship cargoes that cross the vastness of space. But even as the New Republic works to unmake the Empire, ironically, the Empire is trying to make use of the fringe to maintain itself.

The Deep Core Haulers

In the past, the Empire had wealth to spare. Huge container vessels carried countless cargoes to and from Imperial factory worlds, fleets and battle stations. Star Destroyers once could afford the luxury of dumping their refuse before making lightspeed.

However, with troops and material scarce, the Empire can no longer afford such waste. As the most recent Imperial buildup intensified, dependence on bulk freighters increased, yet military forces, busy elsewhere pacifying newly conquered regions, were unable to provide military escort. Those ships that weren't hijacked by pirates often fell victim to Republic privateers.

With no other way to guarantee their supply lines, many of the local governors, Moffs and Admirals had no other course but to hire smugglers and heavily armed independent freighters to ferry their fuels and armaments. This tactic also had the bonus of helping to weaken the smugglers' compact formed by Talon Karrde. However, it would be too easy for someone like Lando Calrissian to take on a cargo only to divert it to a Republic port.

That's where the Deep Core hauler system came in. It offered any ship or crew huge sums, but first they had to undergo rigorous and extensive security checks before a license was granted. Fortunately for the smugglers and traders who apply for these permits, as long as they've done no Rebel contracting, the right sum of money in the right hands can ease the process considerably.

Many tramp freighter captains and honest traders make these lucrative runs. However with the right contacts, it is a quick road for many smugglers to gain (or regain) legitimacy. Once licensed, they are offered immunity from prosecution for other petty crimes and for any actions against the New Republic.

The Spice Trade

Despite Republic and Imperial blockades and official "zero tolerance" measures, the galactic spice trade is quite healthy in the Invisible Market. Of course, with the riches at stake, competition among smugglers has often included dirty tricks of one kind or another. Aside from all the usual things a smuggler must evade (customs frigates, religious zealots, disgruntled customers …), there are newer and deadlier threats to his trade appearing every day. Perhaps the most insidious of these are the spice-jackers.

They keep tabs on smugglers and when they put into port for fuel or repairs, the jackers make their move. They either sneak in and steal the cargo, or inform the local authorities, who seize the cargo or the whole ship and then turn it over to the jackers for a cut. Still others take the violent way, "buying" the ship in exchange for the owner's life. The jackers are unscrupulous and move around frequently to avoid too much attention from other smugglers, who would certainly work together to end the career of such a person.

In the past, spice-jacking was fairly infrequent — most crimelords took a dim view of anything that endangered cargo. Of course, with the constantly shifting power base of the galaxy's criminal organizations, the spice-jackers have been able to operate with much less scrutiny. To make things worse, the Hutt crime clans, eager to regain lost territory and expand their holdings, have hired spice-jackers to work for them since Hutts customarily refuse payment if a shipment is lost.

By sponsoring spice-jackers, who will work for a tenth of the fee a first rate smuggler can demand, they can cut costs dramatically.

Mako Spince

Mako Spince always liked the good life. Born to an important Senator, he was raised to a life of ease. Intelligent, good looking and with plenty of connections, there were many who figured there was no limit to how far Mako could go. The only problem was that Mako knew this. He was all too aware of his father's status and the way it opened doors for him, so Mako never took anything too seriously — except having fun.

"Everything can wait" was his philosophy. This resulted in lower grades in school — he was quite intelligent, but was unmotivated to complete any work. That was why it took him so long to attend the Academy. He knew that he had the talent to go far; it just seemed like there was always something better to do. Fortunately, the Academy has no specific age requirements; when he entered, Mako was fully ten years older than the average cadet in his class.

That average cadet just happened to be Han Solo and the two of them became great friends, horsing around and pulling pranks of all kinds. Of course, one of those pranks got Mako into enough trouble to put him where he is today. Stealing a gram of antimatter from the physics lab, he had intended to blast the Academy Seal off the surface of the "mascot moon," a rocky planetoid in high orbit. Instead, the blast destroyed the planetoid.

Once the culprit was discovered, Mako was expelled after a "show" hearing. Mako was annoyed by this turn of events, but he still had his family's money and there was a whole galaxy out there to mess with. He had made enough contacts at the Academy to establish himself, with a little extra money from his father, as a smuggler. Of course, after his family found out (and after Mako acquired the money he needed from his parents' account), he was cut off from the family trust, but by then Mako had already set course for Hutt space on his new ship.

Mako had quite a reputation as a smuggler. No safe and sturdy cargoes for him; only the most challenging and lucrative would do. Luck was with him when Solo got drummed out of the service a few years later. Seeing what a drag he'd

become, Mako took him to see the vast Corellian Sector of Nar Shaddaa and the young man was hooked.

Eventually Solo decided to head for other areas of space, convinced that he could make more money in an area where there weren't so many smugglers … and so many Imperial patrols. After Solo left, Mako's luck ran out. After a bloody run-in with the Na-Qoit bandits in the Ottega system, he was permanently crippled. No longer able to make the Kessel Run, and knowing his funds weren't long for this universe, he took a job as a Traffic Controller on Nar Shaddaa, which he holds to this day.

Every day, Mako routes hundreds of ships:

freighters, fighters, cruisers, yachts and anything else, all ready to do business with the Hutts. With Jabba dead, Nar Shaddaa has become a center of smuggling in this region of space. What surprised Mako the most was that Solo was apparently one of the ones behind Jabba's death and there was a staggering bounty on his head. He never thought Han had it in him.

When Solo returned to Nar Shaddaa, Mako knew his ship had come in. Sure, he felt guilty turning one of his friends in, but he needed the money. Mako felt even better about it after he knew that Han escaped death once again … and he had the credits from the reward in his pocket.

■ Mako Spince

Type: Crippled Tramp Freighter Captain
DEXTERITY 1D*
Blaster 3D, brawling parry 1D*, dodge 1D+2*
KNOWLEDGE 3D+1
Alien species 7D, bureaucracy 7D+2, cultures 6D, languages 7D+1, planetary systems 9D, streetwise 9D, traffic control procedures 9D
MECHANICAL 1D*
Astrogation 9D+1, beast riding 1D+1*, communications 7D, planetary shields 8D+1, repulsorlift operation 2D*, sensors 8D, space transports 2D+2*, starship gunnery 2D+1*, swoop operation 1D+1*
PERCEPTION 3D+2

The Hearing

Transcript Excerpts From Expulsion Proceedings Against Cadet Mako Spince; Final Session.

Members include Senator Simon Greyshade; Chief Technical Proctor Gandl Vorkosigge; Physics Professor Lucinta Cal-Meg, Student Adviser; and, Academy Dean Horace Wyrmyr

Greyshade: What's the prognosis on the planetoid fragments anyway?

Cal-Meg: Not very good. The orbit still isn't stable either, so we don't know how much will burn up on reentry.

Wyrmyr: Gone! The very symbol of the Academy is gone! Fifty centuries —

Greyshade: Thank you Dean Wyrmyr, we've seen the reports.

Cal-Meg: The placement was very precise if I say so myself …

Wyrmyr: Enough, of this. He blew up a moon!

Greyshade: Well, that's what this proceeding is all about. Cadet Spince, do you have anything to say for yourself?

Spince: (pause) That I'm really sorry … and that I'll never do it again.

Greyshade: (Stifling laugh) That I'll believe.

Vorkosigge: Now listen here young man. This is your future at stake …

Spince: I guess I miscalculated ….

Cal-Meg: You realize you could have vaporized the whole orbital lab when you did this, don't you?

Spince: Well, not really. I collected only a few nanograms at a time — the antimatter was scheduled for detonation any —

Vorkosigge: Detonation at the armaments range. Anything could have gone wrong!

Spince: — anyway. I took precautions.

Greyshade: Precautions, eh? Have you looked up in the sky lately?

Cal-Meg: And destroyed school property for a prank.

Wyrmyr: What would he care? Look at his transcript. You'll see what kind of attitude he's had here.

Vorkosigge: Exactly, we have holos of some of the "stunts" …

Wyrmyr: Disgusting! Who programmed the food dispensers with gene lab samples?

Spince: Harmless …

Wyrmyr: Who faked a broadcast of my own death during homecoming?

Vorkosigge: While the Dean was away on sabbatical.

Spince: We won; he should have watched.

Cal-Meg: (chuckle) That was pretty convincing, wasn't it?

Greyshade: All very fascinating, I'm sure. (Bangs hammer) Order! Order! Can we please get back to the topic at hand?

Wyrmyr: You're not just going to be expelled; you are going to prison, young man! To Kessel, if I have anything to say —

Greyshade: Respectfully, Dean, you don't.

Spince: Please, I realize the trouble I'm in, but …

Greyshade: Cadet Spince, I know what you must be going through now. I was young once, too. Though, not this young, apparently.

Vorkosigge: The Security Bureau should hear of this. It's nothing short of terrorism.

Cal-Meg: Has the ISB checked the matter out?

Greyshade: They have and apparently he can be vouched for with regard to "unmutual" intent or anti-Imperial actions. The statements of both Cadet Solo and the "unidentified" witness have been verified with truth drugs.

Wyrmyr: Spince! You stay away from —

Greyshade: Dean! Please. However, in view of the solemn responsibility I have been charged with, I must concur with my colleagues, and recommend that you be summarily expelled from the Academy and banned from all future Imperial service. In light of your family standing, I shall further recommend that criminal proceedings be dropped.

Wyrmyr: I'll appeal this.

Greyshade: You have that right, but this proceeding is hereby closed. And … Mr. Spince, I recommend you think about what happened here today. Seriously.

Bargain 9D, command 5D, con 8D+2, forgery 7D, gambling 8D, search 6D+1
STRENGTH 2D
Stamina 2D+1*
TECHNICAL 3D+1
Computer programming/repair 7D, first aid 6D, repulsorlift repair 7D
* Some attributes and skills have been lowered because of his accident
Character Points: 10
Move: 5*
* Repulsor chair
Equipment: Repulsor chair, blaster pistol (4D), headset comlink, datapad

Salla Zend

How did a woman like Salla Zend become a smuggler? Just lucky, if you ask her. Salla liked understanding the way things worked and so had always been interested in fixing them. From there, it was only a few steps to becoming a technician. She could have gone far in science and engineering, but there was something about going around in a cleansuit with a portacomp that she just didn't like. She liked being where the action was. So, ultimately, she ended up as a tech on a corporate transport. She liked the limitless promise she could find in every port city and station.

There was a lot more out there than the transport would go to, so she made long-range plans. After a while, she had saved up enough to get a loan, not from a Hutt, but a real loan, to get a ship. She's not exactly sure how she drifted from regular merchant shipping to the smuggling trade, but she can't say she has much to complain about. It's how she met Shug and Lando. And Han.

Han had an easy-going style that she found very attractive. That they could talk the same techno-jargon was a bonus. They shared a friendly rivalry, but it began to become something more than what either had expected. While spending more and more time together, they made no commitments. They were both very young and figured they had all the time in the world. That illusion was almost the death of her.

While making a standard run, her hyperdrive conked out on her and her ship made the reversion to realspace on a collision course with a neutron star. Han was able to save her, but her ship was lost and she was shaken enough to want to retire right then and there. She had hoped she had found the right guy to retire with, but she was mistaken. Han was still too free in his ways and by the time she got his goodbye holomessage, he was light years away.

These days, Salla spends most of her time working on the myriad of ships in Shug's garage. Salla's pride and joy is the *Starlight Intruder,* a highly modified freighter licensed for Deep Core hauling. This ship is how she is going to make her return to the spaceways — and it'll put most any cargo hauler to shame. Han left her life a long time ago, but that feeling of power and speed she felt when flying the *Falcon* has never left her; she is determined to make the *Intruder* the fastest ship in the galaxy. Some say, though never to her face of course, that this single-mindedness is her way of getting back at Solo for leaving her.

Seeing Solo again, and having to save his skin, got to her. The fact that he's married and a father now really disturbed her. She had half-forgotten all those feelings, and then *he* shows up to make her remember everything all over again. Still, it was good to see him finally able to stay in one place for a while.

A woman as skilled or as attractive as Salla will never long for companionship, but a man like Solo is a hard act to follow. Whether Salla's feelings might be rekindled remains to be seen.

■ *Salla Zend*
Type: Smuggler
DEXTERITY 3D+1
Blaster 7D, brawling parry 5D, dodge 7D+2, melee combat 5D+1, melee parry 4D, vehicle blasters 5D
KNOWLEDGE 2D+1
Alien species 7D, bureaucracy 6D, cultures 5D+2, planetary systems 8D, streetwise 8D+1, survival 6D, value 10D
MECHANICAL 3D+2
Astrogation 8D, repulsorlift operation 7D+1, space transports 8D+1, starship gunnery 8D, starship shields 7D
PERCEPTION 3D
Bargain 7D, con 5D+2, gambling 6D, hide 5D+1, search 5D
STRENGTH 3D
Brawling 5D, climbing/jumping 4D+1, stamina 6D
TECHNICAL 2D+2
Computer programming/repair 6D+1, droid programming 6D+1, droid repair 5D+1, repulsorlift repair 6D+2, space transport repair 8D+1

Force Points: 1
Character Points: 10
Move: 10
Equipment: Blaster pistol (4D+2 damage), comlink, tools

Shug Ninx

Shug Ninx was born with black marks against him. Born of mixed parents, with a Corellian father and a mother from the near extinct Theelin races, as a child he experienced the wall of prejudice the Empire built around the children some called "half-breed." Shug would never feel shame for his heritage, but he knew his opportunities were limited.

Still, Shug knew what he wanted was to sail the spaceways, and sail them he would; if the Academy or Scout services were closed to his ambitions, there were other options for a child of half Corellian blood. He had always shown an aptitude for fixing things and spacers would always respect someone who could coax the utmost from a drive unit or shield collator.

It was as a mechanic that Shug eventually found his niche in the universe, working as a lowly tech. Eventually, he saved up enough credits to set up his own place, where he would be working for himself and could set his own rules. Shug had never had much respect for authority and he wanted a place where he could work his business without endless inquiries and licensing. Eventually making it as far as Nar Shaddaa, the so-called "Smuggler's Moon," he found a virtual paradise of opportunity where very few questions were ever asked. In the vertical cities, he created his own "spacebarn," where he built a reputation working miracles with even the most carbonized hulks.

During this time, Shug met many up-and-coming smugglers and eventually became a father figure to the "wild kids" who smuggled or ran blockades for the Hutt gangs. It didn't hurt that he could carouse with the best of them and soon all the best pilots and spacers' mates began spending time around the "barn." This was how he met two spacers in particular, Han Solo and Lando Calrissian. It was also how he met Han's then-sweetheart, Salla Zend.

In time, things changed. Han and Lando headed for other areas of space. Shug made a small fortune working on ships. When Salla had her accident, she wanted a safe, stable place to work, and Shug gladly brought her aboard, eventually making her his business partner.

Over the years, he could afford to be more selective, working for wealthy crimelords and pirate princes and commanding the highest fees. This posed some security problems, but in characteristic fashion, he solved them all and then some. Even his closest friends couldn't believe it when about five years ago he "acquired" the chute as surplus from the second Death Star. Moving it from Bonadan called in a lot of old debts, but once it was installed even the most incredulous had to admit it was a stroke of genius. He even turned a profit by renting out the space in front of the opening as a hologram billboard for a local fizzyglug brand.

Now, Han's back in town, bringing the Rebellion, bounty hunters and a whole lot of fighting with him. Shug hasn't spent much time in space in recent years, and while he feels he's a little old for this kind of action, it's been nice to see his old buddy. Funny though, Shug feels this isn't the last time he's going to see Han.

■ Shug Ninx
Type: Master Mechanic

A SPLIT SECOND LATER THE FALCON ROARS INTO NINX'S REPAIR SHOP -- A MASSIVE SPACER'S GARAGE FILLED WITH DISMEMBERED SHIPS AND THE GREASY CLUTTER OF A LIFETIME.

DEXTERITY 2D+1
Blaster 5D, brawling parry 4D+1, dodge 6D, melee combat 5D, melee parry 5D, vehicle blasters 6D+1
KNOWLEDGE 1D+1
Alien species 5D+2, bureaucracy 7D, cultures 6D, planetary systems 8D+1, streetwise 7D+1, survival 5D, value 7D
MECHANICAL 3D+2
Astrogation 6D+2, repulsorlift operation 6D+1, space transports 7D+1, starship gunnery 7D, starship shields 6D+2
PERCEPTION 3D
Bargain 7D, con 6D, gambling 5D+1, search 6D+2, sneak 6D
STRENGTH 3D
Brawling 5D, climbing/jumping 3D+2, stamina 4D
TECHNICAL 4D+2
Capital ship repair 9D+2, capital ship weapon repair 7D+1, computer programming/repair 7D+2, droid programming 8D, droid repair 8D+2, repulsorlift repair 10D+1, space transports repair 11D+2, starfighter repair 10D+2, starship weapon repair 9D+2
Force Points: 1
Character Points: 14
Move: 10
Equipment: Blaster pistol (4D damage), datapad, mechanic's tools

Lo Khan

Han Solo and Lando Calrissian were barely out of training pants when Lo Khan made the biggest haul of his smuggling career on the Gamor Run. He heard that a rival, Uxbeg, had contracted to carry a load to some goon named Spadda.

Luckily for him, Uxbeg was still busy with a load of bulk yeast paste for the Corporate Sector prison at Star's End. With only a little bit of lying, he managed to intercept Uxbeg's shipment.

He was very surprised to see that it was a spice consignment from the royal governor in Thokosia system to Aikhibba system, one of the minor stopping points on the 'Run. Lo Khan was running low on fuel, but he figured it was better to raise ship than wait for Uxbeg to come back.

He stopped over in the Deneba system to refuel. While there, he ran into Luwingo, a Yaka native he'd met on an earlier run. Luwingo was down on his luck, and Lo Khan had been there many times. He decided to take him along and give him a small cut of the profit. Lo Khan never demanded any payback for the charity. Luwingo earned his pay when Lo Khan had a run-in with Uxbeg's goons.

They were holding over, waiting for final word from Spadda, when Luwingo took a blaster bolt for him. Lo Khan was worried the big guy was history, but he just shrugged it off. Realizing

'Wingo's usefulness and loyalty, Lo Khan had a change of heart and hired him as his full-time bodyguard. A rich guy's gotta have a couple of servants to push around, ya know?

When he got the cargo to Aikhibba, where this Spadda lived, and found out it was *the* Spadda, Hutt ganglord, he should have figured he was in for the short end of the stick. True enough, the slug shortchanged him immensely, but it was still enough to set Lo Khan up for life.

Since then, Khan has amused himself by doing small runs in his ship, the *Hyperspace Marauder,* and getting drunk in the company of old partners. Few in the trade are as lax and calm as he is between runs. If there is such a thing as a laconic smuggler, then Lo Khan is the best in the business.

Lo Khan

KEEP IT TO YOURSELF, BUT *LUWINGO* HERE SAVED MY CAN IN A SHOOTOUT WITH IMPERIALS ON THE GAMOR RUN. I KEEP HIM AROUND FOR *PROTECTION.*

Type: Laconic Smuggler
DEXTERITY 3D
Blaster 5D, brawling parry 4D+1, dodge 5D+1, melee combat 3D+2, melee parry 3D+2
KNOWLEDGE 2D
Alien species 5D+1, bureaucracy 6D, cultures 4D+1, languages 5D+2, planetary systems 7D+1, streetwise 6D
MECHANICAL 4D
Astrogation 5D+1, repulsorlift operation 4D, space transports 7D+1, starship gunnery 4D, starship shields 6D+2
PERCEPTION 3D+1
Bargain 7D, con 4D+2, gambling 5D+2, search 3D+2, sneak 5D
STRENGTH 3D
Brawling 4D, stamina 4D
TECHNICAL 2D+2
Computer programming/repair 5D+1, droid programming 3D, droid repair 3D+2, space transports repair 5D+1, starship weapon repair 4D+1
Character Points: 12
Move: 10
Equipment: Blaster pistol (4D damage), beckon call tied into *Hyperspace Marauder,* comlink, 3,000 credits

Luwingo

The Arkanians are one of the most scientifically-minded species in the entire Colonies region. Centuries ago, they encountered their primitive neighbors, the Yaka. Taking pity on them, they began performing brain enhancement cyborging surgeries on them. Already bulky and strong, the Yaka were soon refashioned into one of the most intelligent and technically deft species in the Republic. They often find their minds buzzing with accelerated thoughts and perceptions, but after a while, the chaotic randomness is quite boring. Now if the Arkanians were really kind, they would have found a cure for boredom. The unexpected side effects of their greatly enhanced intelligence has given the Yaka a twisted view of life and a bizarre sense of humor.

Luwingo sometimes wonders about this. He couldn't say he's had a very bad life. While it hasn't been as enjoyable as he might have hoped, it was far from as bad as could be feared. Many years ago, he had been a programmer on his world, developing programs and software for commercial use. After saving up enough money, he and his family went on a luxury cruise on Galaxy Tours. Unfortunately, the cyborging did nothing for bad luck. Pirates attacked the ship, stunning everyone with knockout gas.

While they looted the ship's vaults and guest rooms, they noticed Luwingo's young children. While adult Yaka are very difficult to physically restrain, the children, smaller and weaker, are another story, and their enhanced brains would make them valuable slaves to whoever was willing to pay a high enough price.

Luwingo decided to go after them. He chose the most effective way to travel the galaxy and meet lowlife scum on a regular basis — smuggling. He procured a ship with some back pay, quit his job, and began taking on smuggling jobs. Unfortunately, he hadn't foreseen just how odd a figure he made as he went about his business. When his funds ran low, he decided to get himself a partner to blend in better. Conveniently, Luwingo had met Lo Khan earlier.

He decided he had found his partner, and some investigation revealed that Mr. Khan was being set up. Nothing wins loyalty like a life saving, so Luwingo went and ambushed the goons in wait, eliminating them all before they could attack Lo Khan. Of course, Luwingo didn't know that a Hutt crimelord was behind all this, so when a second group of goons showed up later, Luwingo found his new friend in danger. The Yaka ended up taking a blaster bolt for Khan, but that cemented a friendship and partnership that was only in its early stages.

Since then, they have been together for a number of years. Khan doesn't do many runs, so Luwingo has time to continue tracking his family down. Of course, the memories of the pirate boarding might impair his investigation, so he keeps them off most of the time by reprogramming his cyborg brain. Of course, this leaves him with not much to think about except hyperdimensional equations — no great shakes — and new strategies for beating the L7 Logician droid (not much of a challenge either). One thing made him feel good inside — thinking of what he would do to the slavers once he caught up with them.

■ Luwingo

Type: Yaka Cyborg
DEXTERITY 3D
Blaster 4D, brawling parry 7D, dodge 3D+1, melee combat 6D, melee parry 6D, vehicle blasters 4D+2
KNOWLEDGE 4D+1
Bureaucracy 5D+2, cultures 4D+2, planetary systems 6D, streetwise 6D, survival 5D, value 7D+1
MECHANICAL 2D+2
Astrogation 5D, communication 6D, repulsorlift operation 6D, space transports 5D+1, starship gunnery 4D+2, starship shields 5D
PERCEPTION 2D+1
Bargain 3D, con 6D, gambling 4D, search 5D
STRENGTH 4D+2
Brawling 7D, climbing/jumping 7D, lifting 10D, stamina 8D
TECHNICAL 5D
Computer programming/repair 9D+2, droid programming 7D+1, droid repair 8D, space transports repair 8D, security 8D+2
Special Abilities:
Cyborg Brain: Yaka have implanted cyborg brains that greatly increase their intelligence (Luwingo's stats reflect this surgery). All Yaka learn and improve *Knowledge* and *Technical* skills at half the normal cost.
Character Points: 6
Move: 12
Equipment: Blaster carbine (5D damage), blast helmet (+1D physical, +1 energy), comlink

Jak Sazz And Grivooga

"You might go to a hundred smugglers' bars and ask a hundred fellow spacers, but you will never hear a good word paid to ol' Jak Sazz. 'What's nastier inside, his mouth or his ship' is a topic that never goes away. I mean everyone's got an opinion. Really, we're always talking about this — just so he don't hear you, or you might get to find out. If you ask me, you're luckier if he eats you …"

— Lo Khan

Jak Sazz has always been a bottom feeder in the food chain of the underworld. Even Hutts balk at contracting him for work. But he has one thing in his favor — he will never refuse a paying job. Any job at all.

In his years, he has been everything from a slaver to a spice-jacker to garbage tech aboard a media cruiser. Lando Calrissian once remarked

WHAT'S THE DEAL HERE, KHAN? THEY NEVER LET THE *DEEP CORE* HAULERS DOCK PLANETSIDE BEFORE.

NTAOBH. HCK HK.

that Jak would haul unshielded antimatter for the right price; unfortunately, the gag got stale once Jak got wind and kept pestering Lando to see if he had any.

Jak Sazz is of a little known species called the Ab'Ugartte, who aren't known for their congeniality; even among them, he is something of an untouchable. Of his nearly uncountable personal vices, including never bathing, is his preference for live food, which he pummels with his oversized hydrospanner, which he has named "Grivooga." This is the same wrench he repairs his rustbucket of a ship with, and he talks to it incessantly. He carries it everywhere he goes; some people would say he carries it into the turboshower, but since there's no proof he's ever had a turboshower, many bets are still uncollected on this.

That Jak Sazz is still up and running around is commonly joked about as confirmation that entropy is winning in the universe, but most still have a healthy respect for

Jak's abilities. They just cut him and his vermin as wide a berth as possible. A crewmate of Jak's once thought the deal with Grivooga was pretty funny, and had the poor judgment to harass Sazz about it. Jak never had much of a sense of humor, but he sure could cook. And Grivooga, as ever, had no complaints. Other mates and partners have learned the lesson well.

■ **Jak Sazz**

Type: Ab'Ugartte Smuggler
DEXTERITY 3D+1
Brawling parry 6D+1, dodge 4D+1, melee combat: Grivooga 7D, melee parry 7D
KNOWLEDGE 2D+1
Bureaucracy 5D, planetary systems 5D+1, streetwise 4D, survival 6D
MECHANICAL 3D+2
Archaic starship piloting 7D, astrogation 5D, space transports 4D+2, starship shields 4D+1
PERCEPTION 3D
Bargain 3D+1, con 4D, gambling 3D+2, sneak 1D*/4D
STRENGTH 3D
Brawling 6D, stamina 5D+1
TECHNICAL 2D+2
Repulsorlift repair 5D+1, security 3D+1, space transports repair 5D+1
Character Points: 5
Move: 8
Equipment: Grivooga (STR+2D+2 damage)
* Only if upwind due to terrible hygiene.

Romort Raort

Romort Raort is a being of simple pleasures: he just likes seeing people suffer. Whether it was as a bully on his homeworld of Irith, shaking down other kids for their lunch money, or today as a spice-jacker, Romort is a brute who really likes his job. That job currently involves tracking down spice smugglers and laying ambushes for them while they wait for clearance to raise ship. He first started out as a kneebreaker for the old Elaginn gang of 'jackers, but since Elaginn had that terrible accident, flexi-pasting himself to a chair and jumping out a window, Romort has had to run things. But as he always said, Elaginn would've wanted it that way.

Through determination and cruelty, Romort has built up the old gang to where they are one of the biggest spice-jacking rings in Hutt space. Eventually, Romort would like to branch out and muscle in on other regions of space, but he will have to bide his time before he has enough influence to challenge the Hutts at their own game. Patience is one of his only virtues: this may take years, but he enjoys his current work, so there's no rush.

Romort has it easy for a spice-jacker because he has contacts in the port authorities of dozens of worlds. By calling on a few friends, he can see where large shipments of spice are headed. Using an ion cannon, kindly "donated" by some Rebel gunrunners, it's an easy matter to hit the ship while in dock and strip it of its cargo while the crew is readied for sale to slavers.

■ **Romort Raort**

Type: Spice-Jacker
DEXTERITY 3D+2
Blaster 6D, brawling parry 7D, dodge 5D, melee combat 6D+2, melee parry 6D+1
KNOWLEDGE 2D
Bureaucracy 7D, intimidation: torture 8D, planetary systems 5D, streetwise 7D+1, streetwise: Nar Shadda 10D, value: slaves 9D, value: spice 10D
MECHANICAL 3D+2
Astrogation 5D, capital ship gunnery 6D, repulsorlift operation 4D+1, space transports 7D, starship gunnery 5D+2
PERCEPTION 3D
Bargain 6D, con 7D, search 8D+1, sneak 5D+2
STRENGTH 2D+2
Brawling 6D, stamina 5D+2
TECHNICAL 3D
Security 5D
Character Points: 15
Move: 10
Equipment: Breather blast helmet (+2D physical, +1D energy, sealed atmosphere processor), blast armor (+2D physical, +1D energy to chest/torso), ammo bandolier, modified blaster rifle (6D damage)

GREETINGS, SOLO.

The Ordeal of Boba Fett

Acrid smoke still bled from the wreckage as Dengar clambered near the pit of Carkoon. Picking his way among fragments, he could see just how bad it had gotten. Not the battle, though that was fierce enough — he'd seen plenty of battles. It was the aftermath that chilled him. Tatooine had legends of night creatures and what they did to the occasional lost soul. He'd never doubt such tales again. Not that he'd spend a day longer here than necessary anyway. If he hadn't been recovering from too much Zeltron spiced wine, he'd have left long ago.

Still, things had a funny way of working out. Boba Fett never was much of a drinker, and he wanted a front row seat for the execution of Solo and Skywalker. By the time Dengar recovered, the big execution party had left for the only real tourist spot in the system. Word had it Jabba'd go out at odd hours just to appreciate his own cruelty.

Only things went very wrong on this particular trip. After that last garbled message, the castle had been in a panic. Half figured the Tuskens got lucky and were coming to finish the job; the rest bought that Gamorrean's drek about Vader in disguise.

Any thought of a rescue party died as a timed computer virus crippled the dungeon computers and hundreds of Jabba's worst captives ran amok. Normally Jabba's goons could deal with this in their sleep, only most of them were Krayt dragon food right about then.

Dengar supposed he could have helped out, but they weren't paying so he wasn't offering. He hid in the empty rancor pit for a few hours 'til the survivors escaped or wreaked

what feeble vengeance they still could. Meanwhile, Dengar began scheming.

It occurred to Dengar that a crimelord as powerful as Jabba would have a lot of wealth lying around. Hmmm …

By the time Dengar got done skulking around the palace, he'd figured out that most of Jabba's wealth was hidden away on a dozen private residences across the galaxy. Even Jabba's private vaults in the palace were just that — private. Magnetically sealed doors to a vault built out of Dreadnaught hull plating. The only way inside was the ident chip.

Of course, Jabba would never let something that valuable out of his sight. Dengar figured it was probably on his person when he got killed. There was only one way to find out.

At first rise, he stole a skiff. Sure, stealing from a Hutt was a bad idea, but nearest he could guess someone had just done considerably worse and gotten away with it. So here he was, in the least pleasant spot in the universe…

Dengar checked the macrobeast detector one more time, hoping the dust hadn't ruined it already. He was getting some screwy readings, something a hundred meters across, and all he could see was sand and crater. Probably a rockmite nest or something. Or something…

Off in the distance was the burning hulk of Jabba's sail barge. A Jawa sandcrawler had already rolled up to it and the hideous scavengers were already stripping hull plating and half-melted pieces of machinery from the wreck.

Dengar laughed. Who would've figured Jabba, biggest gangster in the Outer Rims, would end up as one more grave decoration by a used droid sale? Dengar put the skiff in slow and began to close in on the sail barge, readying his blaster rifle. It was time to show the Jawas who was boss. Then he saw the flare. Who else could it be but …

Revving the engines, he skimmed over and saw … Boba Fett. Well, he guessed it was Boba, never having seen him without armor or clothes. The way he looked now, that was a habit to keep.

"Boba, what happened here?"

"… never … call … me … enhhhhhh … "

That was Fett all right, near the lip of a crevasse. He looked awful, blistered and covered with some sort of knotted fibrous material, like the inside of a wyykmelon. As Dengar clambered on the ledge, for a second he thought he saw Fett's helmet disappear down a hole over the ledge.

Fett was still clutching some kind of flare gun, nothing Dengar recognized though. Out just beyond the ledge and a few hundred meters down was a pile of metal shards. Must be a Jawa dumping ground, if there was such a thing. Fett was surrounded by dozens of metal fragments, corroded smooth and shiny.

Hauling him aboard, he got his first whiff and nearly dumped Fett right there. That kind of smell made you want to burn your own nose off.

Pretty soon, they were making good time back. He'd given Fett four stimshots to no noticeable effect, except making the twitching worse. Once he got to the castle, he tried washing him off, but no go. The fiber stuff, whatever it was, had to be cut off with a vibroblade.

As the medical droids tended to Boba, Dengar could see his wounds more clearly. Those weren't battle wounds; they were sucker marks, like those of the ethersquids of Gyndine, dotting his body. According to the droid, they were attached to Fett's arteries and veins. Some sort of blood exchanging going on. No question, Boba had been swallowed by the Sarlacc itself.

Oddly, Fett's seizures weren't because of exposure or thirst. Fett was apparently well fed, since there were all sorts of food proteins in his blood. The trouble was an allergic reaction to foreign blood types in his system combined with an industrial-grade neuro-toxin. He asked the droid about the blood shifting. The only theory it had was the Sarlacc couldn't digest its own food without help, so it fed its blood into the victims, and the blood slowly broke down their proteins, before re-entering the Sarlacc. Somehow, the blood fed the victims enough nutrients to keep them alive, so the Sarlacc had a constant food source. Meanwhile, the poor victims rolled around and got slowly dissolved.

Dengar shivered as the droid droned on, thinking about the genetic samples in Boba's blood. Some of it matched guys Jabba had iced years ago. All that "digested in the belly of the Sarlacc for a thousand years" yakkity yak was true, and Boba had been in the middle of it. It gave him the chills.

A month later, Fett came out of his coma. Dengar didn't want to think about it when he could hear him discussing escape plans with guys ten years dead. Or ten years-should-be-dead. When Fett was on solid food again, they talked.

"I thought nobody had ever gotten out of that thing …"

"They all tried the obvious way out. I didn't. They all went for the opening; I *made* an exit."

When he finally got his ship into the air, Dengar was relieved. Dengar had tried talking Boba out of going back, but it was no good. Cruising over the Dune Sea, they neared the clearing. A rusted shape was half covered by new sand. They hovered over the only grave Jabba would ever have. Three kilotons was excessive, even by Dengar's standards, but it was good to see Fett being vindictive; it showed he was getting back to normal.

As Tatooine faded from the scopes, the nav computer flickered Nar Shaddaa's coordinates while calculating the jump to hyperspace. Dengar saw Fett relax for the first time in weeks. Now it was payback time.

Boba Fett's Battle Armor

Model: Modified Mandalorian battle armor
Type: Modified personal battle armor
Cost: Not for sale
Availability: Unique
Game Effect:

Basic Suit: Provides +4D to *Strength* for physical attacks, +3D for energy attacks. Covers head, torso and arms. No *Dexterity* penalties.

Wrist Lasers: 5D damage, uses *armor weapons* skill, ranges: 3-5/25/50.

Rocket Dart Launcher: 6D damage, uses *missile weapons* skill, ranges: 3-5/10/25, poison tipped (causes 5D damage for five rounds). Can use alternative poisons and stun serums.

Turbo Projected Grappling Hook: 20 meter lanyard, uses *missile weapons* skill (ranges 0-3/10/20), magnetic grappling "hook."

Flame Projector: 5D damage, uses *armor weapons* skill, creates cone 1 meter wide, variable one to five meters long.

Concussion Grenade Launcher: Grenades cause 6D damage over a five meter blast radius. Uses *missile weapons* skill, ranges are 1-250/350/500, magazine carries 20 grenades.

Jet Pack: Has a Move of 100 meters horizontally, 70 meters vertically. Uses *jet pack operation* skill, base difficulty is Easy, modified by obstacles. Has 20 charges, can expend up to two per round.

Sensor Pod: +2D to *search*.

Infrared/Motion Sensor: Integrated infrared and motion sensor that adds +1D to *Perception* in darkness or with moving objects ahead and to both sides.

Macrobinoculars: Add +3D to *Perception* or *search* for objects 100–500 meters away. Scomp-linked into blaster rifle; reduces range two levels (for example, long range becomes short range).

Sound Sensor: Adds +1D to *Perception* or *search*. This bonus only applies in quiet situations.

Internal Comlink: Can be linked into *Slave II's* control system (with beckon call), adjusted to other standard frequencies. Also has external speaker.

Broad-band Antenna: Can intercept and decode most communications made on standard frequencies. As a result, Boba Fett can patch into shipboard communications.

Winch: Capable of lifting 100 kilograms (Fett and his equipment only).

Sealed Enviro Filter: Filter system can block out harmful molecules, or in case of insufficient or deadly atmosphere, the suit can completely seal, drawing upon a two hour internal supply of oxygen.

Capsule: Little is known of Boba Fett's armor, save that it is probably the most lethal set of personal battle armor in the galaxy. It is based on the armor of a group of Mandalorian warriors, but no one knows if it is authentic or a replica. Fett has taken advantage of very expensive miniaturization technology, allowing him to construct a set of armor that combines devastating firepower and excellent protection with no hindrance to movement.

Bounty Hunters

Far from the watchful eye of the Empire and its clean, orderly, police-state planets, there is a totally different world not patrolled by armed and armored troops, lacking curfews and weapons detectors and sentry droids. Most Imperial citizens never enter this world, moving only in hermetically sealed, environmentally sculpted corridors and mallplexes. But if they left behind their safe luxury liner world for a while, they would see a unique environment with its own rules.

Moving to this other world, one would find the realm of smugglers. And where you find

smugglers, you will find all sorts of illegal activities. Not just the smugglers and their bosses, but those involved in all aspects of the contraband game. The spice sifters who purify and refine the raw material into the final product. Gang lords and their entourages, replete with secret accountants, bodyguards, odalisques, cooks and entertainers.

There are others here, too. Outlaw techs who can secretly upgrade weapon power or graft on entirely forbidden systems. Dealmakers who can fence anything for any price. Computer slicers who can forge identity passes or fake registration forms. And still more ... spice-jackers, pirates, mercs, slavers — all involved in the Invisible Economy. Even ordinary petty criminals, from pickpockets to confidence tricksters can be found in the sleazy and bustling streets of most free spaceports.

And where you find criminals, you will find bounty hunters. Bounty hunters are a hard lot to pin down, as individualistic as they are dangerous. There are hard-bitten ex-soldiers trying to make ends meet and skip tracers who observe suspects and inform on them. There are countless individuals who fit the mold of the traditional bounty hunter: fearless individuals, with an array of deadly weapons and attitude to match. They travel widely, often keeping a few safehouses, just in case ...

Once, the Empire tried to live up to its ideal of total law enforcement. Garrisons were deployed on a thousand worlds; millions of new prison cells were built. Still, it was never enough. Too many spaces were reserved for crimes of thought and expression, and not enough for murderers or thieves. So the Empire tried using small, mass-produced droids called "seekers" to handle the flood of lawlessness, but to no avail. Independent mercenary armies and planetary peace forces kept order; bounty hunters tracked down the most dangerous criminals.

Bounty hunters inevitably skirt the law. Most give the appearance of working within the law, taking care to get the appropriate permits, but almost all of them end up taking jobs of questionable legality and dubious morality. Many of them openly flout the law, taking contracts as hit men for ganglords and the like.

On many planets, it is easy to find bounty hunters, relaxing, recuperating or ... stalking their prey.

■ Boba Fett

Type: Bounty Hunter
DEXTERITY 4D
Armor weapons 6D, blaster 9D, brawling parry 5D*, dodge 6D*, grenade 6D+1*, melee combat 5D+2*, melee parry 5D*, missile weapons 6D+2, thrown weapons 5D+2, vehicle blasters 7D

KNOWLEDGE 2D+2
Alien species 5D, bureaucracy 5D+2, cultures 5D, intimidation 8D+1, languages 5D+2, planetary systems 6D, streetwise 8D, survival 6D, value 6D+1, willpower 7D+2
MECHANICAL 2D+2
Astrogation 6D+1, beast riding 6D, jet pack operation 6D+1, repulsorlift operation 5D, repulsorlift operation: speeder bike 6D, space transports 7D, starship gunnery 8D, starship shields 6D
PERCEPTION 3D
Bargain 7D, command 4D+2, con 6D, gambling 6D, hide 5D, investigation 9D+2, persuasion 7D, search 8D+2, sneak 6D+2

STRENGTH 3D+2
Brawling 5D*, climbing/jumping 4D, lifting 4D*, stamina 5D*, swimming 5D
TECHNICAL 2D
Armor repair 6D, computer programming/repair 4D, demolition 6D, droid programming 4D, security 8D, space transports repair 6D
* Some of Boba Fett's skills have been reduced because of the Sarlacc's neurotoxins. It is unknown how long this effect will last.
Force Points: 5
Dark Side Points: 7
Character Points: 26
Move: 10
Equipment: Battle armor (see sidebar), blaster rifle (6D damage), comlink, Wookiee scalps dangling from belt, *Slave II*

■ Dengar
Type: Bounty Hunter
DEXTERITY 4D
Blaster 7D, dodge 7D, grenade 6D+1, vehicle blasters 5D+2
KNOWLEDGE 2D+2
Bureaucracy 5D+2, cultures 5D, languages 5D+2, planetary systems 6D, streetwise 5D+2, survival 5D, value 5D+1

MECHANICAL 2D+2
Beast riding 6D+1, repulsorlift operation 6D, starship gunnery 5D, swoop operation 7D
PERCEPTION 3D
Bargain 4D+2, command 4D+2, con 6D, gambling 6D, search 5D+2, sneak 5D+2
STRENGTH 3D+2
Brawling 7D, climbing/jumping 4D+2, lifting 4D+2, stamina 5D+2, swimming 5D
TECHNICAL 2D
Demolition 6D, droid programming 4D, repulsorlift repair 5D, security 6D
Force Points: 1
Character Points: 13
Move: 9
Equipment: Blaster rifle (5D+2 damage), concussion grenades (7D damage), vibroblade (STR+2D damage), flexi-steel binding wire, blast armor (+2D+2 physical, +1D+2 energy to torso, arms and legs), chest-mounted comlink

Dyyz Nataz and Goa

Long before the Empire, there were those who saw the widespread crime and degeneracy in the galaxy and tried to put a stop to it. Everyone is familiar with the Jedi Knights, but they weren't the only ones to enforce the laws of the Republic. The Jedi were too few and often too involved in cosmic menaces to handle every incidence of crime and abuse. To fill this gap, the Senate empowered regional governors to appoint special groups to integrate the legal establishments on each world. Such men were system police authorities, the Sector Rangers and Special Enforcement Officers.

It was a thankless job, not as popular as local planetary investigators, nor as highly regarded as the Jedi Knights. It was for this reason that they largely escaped the growing influence of the Empire. During the early days of the New Order, the Jedi were exterminated. On the other hand, many of the constabularies of citizen worlds were absorbed into the vast machine of the Imperial military and police forces.

Because they fell through the cracks of Imperial control, they survived for a number of years in a state of relative independence. Two such men were Dyyz Nataz and Goa.

Dyyz had risen through the ranks of his system's police forces with a reputation for a tough-as-nails manner and a way of dealing with violent sociopaths. Some said he was too young or too intense for the job, but no one could say he didn't get his perp. Even if there wasn't much left.

He was assigned the rank of Sector Ranger and given power to hunt criminals across his

The denizens of Nar Shaddaa. While Han and Leia head toward his old apartment, Romort Raort (middle) observes from a distance while Spurch "Warhog" Goa (far right) and Dyyz Nataz (right) go about their business.

sector. It was during one such case that he ran across Goa.

Goa, a Diollan ex-mercenary, was then an investigator for Naval Intelligence. During the inquest of a suspected murder aboard an orbital base, he met the suspect, a drill instructor named Thaffe. Solving the crime and absolving Thaffe of guilt, the two had become friends. When Goa mustered out, he got a job working for the Grand Moff's security department. When Thaffe retired, the two volunteered to become rangers. For five years, they made the occasional headline stopping slave rings and pirates.

Thaffe had trained Nataz in anti-terrorist procedure two years previously, so when they ran across each other, both on separate jurisdictions and warrants, they agreed to cooperate. The grim Nataz had found the hide-out of a counterfeit credit ring on an abandoned ore freighter. None of them suspected it was all a set up by Jabba the Hutt, who'd been harassed once too often by overzealous investigators.

When they snuck in, Gank Killers, one of the favored bodyguards of the Hutts, ambushed them. The rangers endured hours of torture without revealing the information Jabba wanted. Finally tiring of them, the Gank Killers decided to kill them one at a time. They made them play sabacc to see who would die first. Thaffe intentionally threw the game to save his partner. As the Ganks shot him on the spot, Goa went berserk and freed himself. In the fracas, Nataz broke free as well and the two made short work of the Ganks. Then they turned on the engines, set course for Jabba's in-system palace asteroid and escaped. The freighter exploded, blowing

the asteroid to bits. Although Jabba wasn't personally there at the time, it earned Nataz the nickname "Megadeath."

In the scandal that followed, both Megadeath and Goa were relieved of duty. Of course, Jabba had levied an impressive bounty on their heads, but teamed together they easily handled all the bounty hunters who came after them. They started recycling the gear from the dispatched hunters and set out to become bounty hunters themselves. Ironically, their exploits have proven so spectacular that a local youth band has adopted Dyyz as a mascot character; he doesn't care as long as they obey the law.

Dyyz Nataz

Type: Bounty Hunter
DEXTERITY 4D
Blaster 7D+1, blaster artillery 5D+1, brawling parry 6D, dodge 5D+1, melee combat 7D, vehicle blasters 8D
KNOWLEDGE 2D+2
Alien species 4D+1, intimidation 5D+1, law enforcement 6D+2, planetary systems 5D+1, streetwise 9D+1, willpower 3D+1
MECHANICAL 2D+2
Repulsorlift operation 6D, space transports 4D
PERCEPTION 3D
Bargain 4D+1, investigation 7D+2, search 5D+1, sneak 7D
STRENGTH 3D+2
Brawling 6D+2, stamina 7D
TECHNICAL 2D
Blaster repair 5D, demolition 5D, first aid 3D+1, security 6D+1
Character Points: 8
Move: 8*
* Due to bulk of armor; 10 without armor.
Equipment: Blaster rifle (5D+1 damage), detonite (10 charges, 5D damage each), blast armor (+2D+2 physical, +1D energy, -1D *Dexterity* and related skills; internal comlink; sealed enviro/atmosphere system; concealed, forearm mounted vibroknives (STR+1D damage, uses

melee combat skill, Easy difficulty to hit); heat projector (causes 5D damage to anyone who touches armor, can only work for two rounds), 3 medpacs, 2 weeks rations, 3 pairs magbinders, 750 credits

■ Spurch "Warhog" Goa

Type: Diollan Merc
DEXTERITY 3D+2
Blaster 5D, grenade 6D, vehicle blasters 5D+1
KNOWLEDGE 2D+2
Intimidation 5D+1, streetwise 6D, survival 4D+1, value 3D+2
MECHANICAL 2D+2
Beast riding 7D+1, repulsorlift operation 5D, walker operation 5D
PERCEPTION 2D+1
Command 4D+2, gambling 3D+1, investigation 7D+1, search 6D, sneak 5D+2
STRENGTH 3D+2
Brawling 5D+1, climbing/jumping 4D, lifting 7D+2, stamina 6D+1, swimming 8D
TECHNICAL 3D
Demolition 6D+2, droid repair 5D+1, security 6D+1
Character Points: 4
Move: 10
Equipment: Blaster rifle (5D damage), blast armor (+2D physical, +1D energy all locations except front of head), 3 medpacs, comlink, survival gear, 500 credits

Scavengers

War is big business, and not just for weapons manufacturers. Even after the ion guns and blasters have fallen silent, there is still wealth to be acquired on the battlefield for the junk trader. Huge fortunes can be made by salvaging the remains of vehicles and artillery emplacements and from stripping combat gear from the dead. Sometimes equipment can be repaired and resold; if an item as a whole cannot be repaired, parts can often be stripped and sold off individually. In rare cases, scavengers may come across secret weapons that can be studied and duplicated for later sale. Even burned-out wrecks can turn a profit on the bulk metal market.

The following is a report filed on the scene by New Republic journalist Rivoche Tarkin, from the Emancipator *at Coruscant …*

War is sometimes likened to the battles of the great beasts of prey. There are the long, drawn-out periods of stalking, which end in a sudden flash of muscle and fang. So it has been with the current Galactic Civil War. Once the underdog Rebels, the New Republic has gained a second wind and tears into its opponent with all its ferocity. On the other, the mighty Empire has fallen and is cornered. And like a cornered predator, it is killing itself to destroy its enemy.

If this metaphor seems apt in this regard, consider how well it applies to the aftermath. In nature, after the hunter has had his fill, the lesser beasts crowd in to feed on the remains. Just so, in all wars there are people who exploit the carnage for their own gain. This is no different now, as Empire and Republic clash, than it was millennia ago during the chaos of Xim's reign. Whole planets may be laid waste and fleets of wreckage float lifelessly in the void; still-warm fragments of Death Star may tumble alongside the cold splinters of the *Eibon Scimitar*.

To most, this is grim reminder of the inability of civilizations to behave in a civilized manner, but to some, it is opportunity. They see the untended wreckage not as memorial, but as a fortune in the making. Like the scavengers of nature, these war scavengers, or "scavs" as they are sometimes called, move in after the battle had died down. They wait in the wings, too weak to participate, but patient, knowing that at some point the fighting will cease and then they can swoop in to take what they will …

When any small conflict erupts, as in the five-hundred-year feud between the Botor and their neighbors, the Dawferim, renegades and scavengers come from nearby systems. When galactic war breaks out, scavengers can appear from

WHEN SOCIAL ORDER COLLAPSES -- EVEN AN *UNJUST* SOCIAL ORDER -- PILLAGERS AND *THIEVES* ALWAYS RISE TO THE OCCASION --

every nook and cranny of the civilized universe looking for something of value.

No matter their origin, scavengers are some of the most loathsome and immoral beings in the galaxy. Looting equipment, they ignore wounded and dying soldiers to steal the last precious fragments remaining on a battlefield. During the Galactic Civil War, both Empire and Rebellion have had to deal with scavengers, and in many cases have done so harshly. After the Battle of Hoth, the icy plains were covered with scavs collecting weapons and gear for resale or for personal use. Both Rebels and Imperials have made it a general policy to treat them as combatants and fire on them as soon as they appear.

Aside from the ethical concerns, there is a pragmatic reason to treat scavs like criminals. Valuable information about how a battle was won or lost can be thoughtlessly destroyed. Sometimes the wounded are further injured or even killed as the scavengers cross the battlefield in search of plunder. Often scavs are so eager to get at the booty before someone else gets it, they sneak in while the battle is still in progress. Using recovered warcrawlers and weapons, they will attack any small or weak group. Poorly armed medical and escape vehicles are fair game and on several occasions, holomedia reporters and crews have been gleefully attacked.

NEKS-- CYBORREAN BATTLE DOGS... KEPT IN RESERVE BY THE CANNY SCAVS FOR A MOMENT LIKE THIS!

The typical scavenger is reasonably well-armed, but usually has more armor and weapons than skill. They carry large pouches of tools to jury-rig things as needed, and may have any number of exotic things stolen from the dead; they use whatever is convenient and will get the job done. For example, scavs may use Cyborrean battle dogs for protection, while using stolen or remanufactured ground vehicles for transport.

■ Typical Scavenger
Type: Scav
DEXTERITY 2D
Blaster 4D, dodge 4D+2, grenade 3D+1, vehicle blasters 3D+2
KNOWLEDGE 1D+2
Planetary systems 3D, streetwise 4D+1, survival 4D+2, value 5D
MECHANICAL 2D+1
Repulsorlift operation 4D
PERCEPTION 2D
Bargain 5D, search 4D+2, sneak 4D+1
STRENGTH 2D
TECHNICAL 3D
Blaster repair 5D, computer programming/repair 4D+1, demolition 4D, droid repair 5D, ground vehicle repair 4D, hover vehicle repair 4D+2, repulsorlift repair 5D+2, security 5D+1, space transports repair 4D+2, starship weapon repair 5D+2
Character Points: Varies, typically 0-5
Move: 10
Equipment: Blaster rifle (5D damage), tools, medpac, comlinks, survival kit, fusion welder (5D damage), laser torch (5D damage), blast helmet (+1D physical, +1 energy), blast vest (+1D physical, +1 energy)

■ "Nek" Cyborrean Battle Dogs
Type: Trained Attack Animal
DEXTERITY 2D
PERCEPTION 3D
STRENGTH 2D+2
Brawling 4D+2
Special Abilities:
  Body Armor: Add +2D to *Strength.*
  Teeth: Do STR+2D+1 damage.
  Claws: Do STR+1D damage.
Move: 12
Size: .9–1.3 meters long

Capsule: Neks are very aggressive creatures that are used by many scavengers, including those on Coruscant. They are the product of genetic and cybernetic engineering and originate on the heavy grav planet of Cyborrea. They are given computer and bionic treatments to enhance their combat skills and are fearless in combat. They like to leap onto their prey and bite deeply using their multiple rows of razor sharp teeth. While gripping with the mouth, they then rake cyborg claws along the victim's body.

Chapter Four
The Force

Overview

Light and Dark Aspects

The ancient mystics of the galaxy have long studied the omnipresent nature of the Force. These scholars and philosophers discovered that the Force was the essence of the universe's cycle of existence, part of life and death in nature. All things in existence are a part of it, but none so much as living, sapient beings. They further learned that with years of patient study, the Force could eventually be manipulated by individuals in a way that defied rational explanations. Because the Force is everywhere, there are no limits to the feats that could be achieved if the being using the Force was knowledgeable enough of its way. Beings could communicate across vast distances, heighten their senses and see past the veils of time.

These learned ones preserved their knowledge and established traditions to train their descendants and increase their understanding. These great traditions of enlightenment came to flourish across the galaxy. Many of them focused on particular qualities of the Force or on different disciplines that were but one of many ways of knowing the Force. Still, most of these scholars do agree on basic principles. To better understand the ways of the Force, these scholars characterized it by its two most fundamental aspects: the Light Side and the Dark Side.

The Light is positive. It is intimately bound with the essence of living things; it is peace, harmony and knowledge. The Light Side springs from the great pattern of existence. It draws strength from diversity and tolerance. It is also inherently communal in nature, thriving on cooperation. Those emotions that enhance the existence of the whole flow from it and tap into its great reserves of strength and peace. Patience, humility and self-sacrifice are paths to enlightenment. Above all, it seeks harmony and perfection.

The Dark Side, in comparison, is the force of entropy and destruction. Chaos and rage feed it and are its sources of power. The Dark Side is a part of nature — it is not inherently evil, but evil comes from its irrationality, its intolerance and its lack of control. Bestial and predatory, domination is its goal. Mercilessly aggressive and unforgiving, its adherents are blinded by greed and lust for power over those weaker than themselves.

The Light and Dark Side manifest themselves in the way they are used; they are simply different interpretations of a single aspect of nature, and they exist in balance with themselves and the universe.

Just as with any aspect of life and death, both the Dark Side and the Light Side are intertwined with each other, are necessary to each other and form a cosmic balance. The important matter is avoiding the emotions of anger and hate which summon the Dark Side. By concentration, it is possible to go beyond desire and emotion, and thereby grow very powerful in the Light Side of the Force. Then great things are possible.

The Light Side

The Light Side is the essence of creation, balance and growth. It is peace and tranquillity flowing through the universe. Aside from the path of the Jedi, there are hundreds and perhaps thousands of unique paths to the Light practiced by masters and pupils throughout the galaxy over the ages. The Jedi were not the oldest, but they were the longest lasting, the most famous and the most effective in preserving the ways of the Light Side against those who struggled to bring darkness. In this, they found similarity with their non-Jedi fellows.

None can say for sure where the Jedi came from. Some believe that Ossus, a planet in the Adega System, may have been their first home. Certainly the fortress there was an important stronghold millennia ago since that was one of few places to obtain the exotic jewels used in lightsabers before the technology existed to synthesize them. It is possible that the Order may have begun there, but what is not known is why Ossus was abandoned 4,000 years ago. Now, Ossus is a world of ruins and peaceful but technologically primitive inhabitants.

Those who study the Light Side are drawn to nature and often take up residence in areas of unspoiled natural beauty. It is important for them to be surrounded by life. Whether they choose a cottage in a meadow, a hut in a swamp or an austere yurt on a vast desert plain, the bond of all beings to their surroundings is a strong trait in all who study the Force.

Throughout history, Jedi were called upon to take up arms to fight injustice and to maintain order, yet in times of peace, many often preferred to take up lives of quiet contemplation. Meditation and artistic pursuits were some of the ways they could focus their concentration upon growing stronger in the Force. Some Jedi spent lives filled with action, solving great riddles, and bringing law. Others preferred to spend lives of single-minded self-purification, honing themselves for a single great act of incredible difficulty. All are equally valid paths to enlightenment.

Though they have been largely wiped out from the galaxy, there are some students and even at least one Jedi Master who escaped the attention of the Emperor and his servants. Some escaped because they were too weak to attract notice. Others found ways to hide their presence from his notice, and still others were too distant for him to reach. Still, there are very few Jedi, most prominent of them Luke Skywalker, hero of the New Republic. Skywalker and his sister Leia are leading the effort to resurrect the ancient fellowship of the Jedi. They may be the hope of the galaxy.

The Jedi Holocron

The Jedi Holocron is one of the greatest of the Jedi Artifacts of the Modern Era known to have survived the Great Purge. Its origin is shrouded in mystery, but some facts are known. At its most basic level, it is a primitive hologram recorder, storing information and playing it back as a sort of library.

As Obi-Wan Kenobi taught to Luke, "The teachings of the Holocron include thousand-year-old-secrets — but they also include the words and faces of men in the process of discovery. The

...A BROTHER AND SISTER BORN TO WALK THE SKY, BUT RECKLESS BROTHER FALLS-- INTO DARK SIDE'S EYE! JEDI SISTER CARRIES HOPE FOR FUTURE IN HER WOMB. ONLY SHE CAN SAVE THE SKYWALKERS FROM CERTAIN DOOM!

A JEDI-KILLER WANTS TO TAME HER. NOW THE DARK SIDE LORD COMES TO CLAIM HER. SHE MUST BATTLE JOIN AGAINST THIS THIEF, OR THE DYNASTY OF ALL THE JEDI WILL COME TO GRIEF!

Jedi Masters of old were not afraid to let their minds roam freely, for they were hungry for ever greater understanding of the mysterious Force which had become their power and their ally."

The Holocron's importance is belied by its simple appearance. On further examination, its ancient and powerful nature reveals itself. Constructed of ancient gemstones, it is a smooth cube that fits comfortably in the palm of one's hand. If examined closely, ancient writings glint faintly across an elegantly tooled surface. It glows with a slight, soothing bluish aura, and feels warm, almost alive, to the touch.

To the uneducated or skeptical, it is a mere bauble or a plaything of dim flickers and imperceptible music. Only those who have been awakened to the Force can summon the power of the Holocron. While Dark Side users can call forth some of the knowledge it holds, the deeper mysteries can only be unlocked by a properly trained Jedi Knight of the Light Side.

Those who have the awareness to make use of it awaken the power of organic crystals deep inside the Holocron. They first find the image of Bodo Baas, famed Jedi Master of long ago. He is the "Gatekeeper" of the Holocron's most useful hidden function — that of an interactive teaching tool. Almost without bidding, the Holocron can sense the surface thoughts of the user and present the wisdom of the ages.

Bodo Baas is only the first of many Jedi Masters whose wisdom dwells within the storage molecules of the Holocron, but until the user has gained enough wisdom, he is the only one encountered. Knowledge is power and the makers of the Holocron knew that too much in the hands of the unprepared could be the undoing of all their work. If the user only seeks basic knowledge, then there is no difficulty and its lore may be accessed directly, like a computer encyclopedia, or by hearing the words of the Masters themselves as told by Bodo Baas. Deeper teachings and accounts are told directly by other Masters.

For hundreds of years, it was believed lost. What was not known was that it was in the possession of Ashka Boda, a great and famous Jedi in his own right. Ashka Boda was captured by the Emperor and slain many years ago, and the Holocron became the Emperor's tool. It is feared that the Emperor has gained much of his knowledge from it.

Vima-Da-Boda

The Skywalkers are far from the only family that has a tradition of the Force flowing in their blood. One such family is that of Vima-Da-Boda. From the time of her great-great-great-grandmother, the legendary Vima Sunrider, the women of her line have been destined for greatness.

For nearly a century, Vima was an illustrious woman warrior, serving the Republic to the best of her ample capabilities. Bringing justice, fighting evil and protecting the innocent, she was one of the great Jedi of her age. A greatness she eventually wished to pass on.

Knowing the blood of some of history's great Force users flowed through her veins, it was her hope that her daughter, Neema, could follow in her footsteps and become a Jedi. She began training her daughter at an early age, just as her mother had taught her. At first, it seemed that Neema would indeed carry the tradition to another generation. By the time she was a young woman, she was very powerful indeed. Neema showed more promise in the Force than her mother had, but sadly, she would choose not to follow the path of the Jedi.

Neema wasn't satisfied with her exceptional progress. She hungered to master in a few years what often took decades and perhaps centuries. But Neema wouldn't wait for the eventual wisdom her mother spoke of. At first, she allowed herself to use her own ambition and impatience to amplify her learning, and indeed her learning accelerated.

What she didn't understand was that she had tapped into the power of the Dark Side. So gradual was her corruption that her mother wasn't aware of it till its grasp on Neema was nearly unbreakable. Neema hadn't actually begun the use of the Force for evil purposes, but her intentions were those that led down that pathway and soon she fell in with a group of likeminded, rebellious Jedi. From there, her surrender was complete.

Vima tried to undo this, but found her once loving daughter contemptuous and cruel. She even became the mistress of an Ottethan warlord who courted her friends to gain their aid. He was the autocratic ruler of a dozen systems on the very distant edge of the galaxy. Barbaric and capricious, he was unfaithful to Neema with her own friends, but she would hear nothing of leaving him despite, or perhaps because of, her mother's pleas.

Finally, as an ultimate repudiation, she wed this despot in a splendidly primitive ceremony. Vima could only accept her daughter's decision and hope she would come to her senses. After a few months on his throne planet, his charms wore thin. Initially thrilled by his crude manners, Neema began to despise his ignorance and vulgarity. Tired of her, he eventually cast her aside for the dozen others he kept around his keep.

Enraged at his treatment of her, she used her Dark Side powers against him.

And failed.

He had learned primitive defenses against the Force from Neema's former friends. He humiliated her, throwing her into his oubliette, where she languished for months. Weeping in her cell, Neema repented her foolish ways and summoned her reserves to send her thoughts out to the one who would still care — her mother, Vima.

Horrorstruck, Vima rushed to the Ottethan system, willing to pay any price or do anything to release her daughter. She arrived too late. The warlord had bored of Neema and let her loose in the savage forests, where Rancors ran wild.

Seeing his contemptuous mock pity, Vima gave way to rage and killed him with a single stroke of her lightsaber. His guards ran in fear from Vima, but all she felt now was emptiness and despair.

This was how Vima-Da-Boda came to lose her connection to the Force. As she sank deeper into misery and guilt, she disappeared; a great Jedi vanished at a time when the galaxy needed her. Then came the Great Purge, when Palpatine and Vader slew the Jedi. Fearing for her life, Vima ran and disowned her own greatness and

was, in turn, forgotten. Today she lives in a gutter on Nar Shaddaa, surrounded by apathy and contempt.

Little do most of her neighbors suspect just how great a person Vima was. Only a woman from another world would ever suspect. That woman was Leia Organa Solo, Jedi student and heroine in her own right. Vima could see, amidst her own weakening faculties, the power for good in Leia, mirroring her own once glorious past. Vima sought out Leia and passed on a precious gift, her own lightsaber, an ancient weapon a hundred centuries old. Without a doubt, Leia has not seen the last of Vima-Da-Boda.

■ Vima-Da-Boda
Type: Fallen Jedi
DEXTERITY 2D+2
Dodge 4D, lightsaber 6D
KNOWLEDGE 3D+1
Alien species 7D, cultures 6D, languages 6D, planetary systems 8D, streetwise 11D, survival: Nar Shaddaa 7D
MECHANICAL 2D

PERCEPTION 3D+1
Bargain 5D, con 5D, search 7D+2, sneak 6D
STRENGTH 2D+2
Stamina 4D
TECHNICAL 2D
First aid 3D, lightsaber repair 6D+2
Special Abilities:
Force Skills: Control 12D, sense 12D, alter 11D
These are only some of the powers which Vima-Da-Boda has so far demonstrated:
Control: Absorb/dissipate energy, emptiness, hibernation trance
Sense: Life detection, life sense, receptive telepathy, sense force
Alter: Telekinesis
Control and Sense: Lightsaber combat, projective telepathy
Control, Sense and Alter: Force harmony
Control and Alter: Control another's pain*, transfer Force
*Described in the *Dark Force Rising Sourcebook*.
This character is Force-sensitive.
Force Points: 8
Dark Side Points: 4
Character Points: 15
Move: 8
Equipment: Lightsaber (5D damage), sack filled with various trinkets, robes
Note: Many of Vima's skills have been lowered due to age, disuse and her own despair.

The Dark Side

Unlike the Light Side of the Force, which embraces the whole, the entire focus of the Dark Side is the self. The appeal of the Dark Side is its very destructiveness and its isolation. Those who seek power for selfish reasons find comfort in its narcissistic gaze. The Dark Side emphasizes aggrandizement of self to the exclusion of others. In this way, rage and anger are turned into sources of strength.

Many are attracted to the Dark Side because its *selfish* nature allows great and showy deeds. The ease with which power is summoned belies its danger, for anger and hatred consume the individual even as one dominates one's surroundings. Ultimately, the Dark Side rejects the very celestial nature of life itself. To the Jedi, the Force is not a part of their existence; it *is* their existence. To a student of the Dark Side, this is incomprehensible.

It is not uncommon for Dark Side students to go into the wilderness, much as their Light Side counterparts do. The crucial difference is that the Light Jedi goes into the wilderness to commune with the wild. The Dark Side follower goes to separate himself from the community of life. There, in isolation, a Dark Side follower can perfect his or her own oneness with the Dark Side, and revel in that corruption. Yet, in the Dark Side are anger and hatred and isolation and … fear. That fear drives the Jedi to isolation, jealousy and the desire to be the most powerful of all.

This very predatory nature sparks battles of dominance when several Dark Jedi or Dark Side Adepts gather. Sometimes these are violent confrontations, other times they involve subtle mind games or diplomatic discussions; but make no mistake, there will be some attempt to assert control over each other. The violent nature of the Dark Side often leads to betrayal and bloodshed.

Not only does this fratricidal tendency discourage long term cooperation among Adepts, it also has hindered the passing of knowledge. Whereas the Jedi and other servants of the Light Side have established great libraries and oral traditions to advance their work and educate succeeding generations, those of the Dark Side have few such institutions. Many never record their knowledge for fear it may aid an enemy. Others are too arrogant to allow others to learn from their mistakes.

The current period is not the only time servants of evil have used the Force for vast power. The Dark Side's influence has waxed and waned throughout history. This is what the Jedi Holocron has to say about the Dark Side:

"A Jedi does not grasp at power.
A Jedi is not a dominator, not an oppressor.
To grasp for power is to abandon
the Ways of the Force.
Such a one ceases to know the Force, except
in his Dark Side.
To grasp at power is to take up the
path that leads to destruction.
The Dominator is the enemy, yes.
But the Jedi do not use the dark powers of the
dominator against him."

— Bodo Baas

This quotation is important to understand the Dark Side. It hints at the temptations of conquest and domination that the Dark offers. There have been many who have served the Dark Side, but not all of them have sought to rule the universe as Palpatine has. There are many, like the Krath, who were content to rule a small region of the galaxy. Others, like Ulic Qel-Droma, simply spread death and destruction on a genocidal level. Many, like the clone Joruus C'baoth, have been driven insane by it and have dominated only the chaos in their minds.

Only Palpatine has been able to spread his darkness completely and totally over an entire galaxy. What has proven to be the lasting genius of Palpatine as Emperor is his devotion to collecting all the knowledge of the Dark Side that he can, as well as what Light Side information he can corrupt and preserve. He is no more altruistic than any other, but his newfound immortality has given him the patience that all before him have lacked.

A Warning About The Dark Side

"Jedi. Hear the Words of Bodo Baas!
"Some among us have thought to conquer the Dark Side by learning its secrets …
"Three, to my knowledge, three have tried this … perished, every one of them perished."

Conquering The Dark Side From Within

A nagging question for Jedi Master and scholar alike is the finality of the Dark Side. There have been those who were only going into a larger world when the Dark Side beckoned and they answered. According to the words of Bodo Baas, as revealed in the Jedi Holocron, there have been only a few who have left the company of the Light to learn the Dark Side's power firsthand and find its weaknesses. There have only been three cases of those who, as fully trained Jedi, have embraced the Dark Side to learn its secrets and intended to use the Darkness upon itself.

Of these, Leia learned of one, Ulic Qel-Droma, and of him only the most superficial knowledge. With the noblest of intentions and the purest of heart, he went among the Krath, only to become what he had set out to destroy, a master of destruction and death. He conquered star systems and became a renegade in the eyes of his fellow Jedi.

But even in this, the answer seems clear — the Dark Side consumes all who embrace it. Just as Ulic was destroyed, so were the others. Master Yoda himself had told Luke that once a being became enamored of the Dark Side, it would forever dominate him, tempting him to fall under its sway. Obi-Wan said as much when he warned Luke of the Emperor and Darth Vader. Luke was told that he must confront his father, perhaps destroy him, but to become too close to him, to try to understand too closely what he had gone through, was to risk madness.

Still, when Luke, if only momentarily, gave in to rage at the Emperor and swung his lightsaber blade down to finish the old man, he found Vader's blade already blocking his. Luke relented and tried to avoid any further surrender to the Dark Side, but Palpatine knew the Skywalker anger too well. He had foreseen just how powerful Luke could be if he turned to the way of destruction. More powerful than Vader. So it was only with the greatest difficulty that Luke pulled back from the abyss. And the man that Vader had once been was reborn.

Perhaps this gave Luke a sense of confidence he didn't deserve, for convinced that he could learn the Dark Side's secrets and destroy it from within, he finally accepted the mantle of Darth Vader as his own. And it was Leia, and her unborn child, who saved him from eternal Darkness.

The Dark Side Compendium

While his Vizier and ministers maintained the day-to-day operation of the Empire, Palpatine spent decades, frequently in seclusion, in meditation and study on a masterwork of his thoughts and teachings. No one can say when he first began work, but his advisors suspect it dates back to the time he first embraced the Dark Side. Numerous beings have succumbed to its temptation over millennia, but few have ever pursued its power as relentlessly as Palpatine.

The Dark Side, as far as its servants are concerned, is obviously stronger and easier than the Light. What Palpatine realized was that the Dark Side had never gained the fame the Light held because it was a personal, secretive thing. The Light was good for simple tricks and for the altruistic, but such things were useless to one who knew the things the Force made one capable of.

Palpatine became convinced the Dark Side was ignored because few had the courage to pay the price it demanded. Since the Dark Side didn't lend itself to sharing and other such weak-minded attitudes, there had not been organizations of Dark Side servants to endure the ages. There was no great collection of Dark Side lore, nor any gathering of its masters. Realizing the task that lay before him, Palpatine knew he must begin at once to attain control over the Dark Side.

With the resources of a galaxy at his disposal, he gathered the greatest works of knowledge from over a million worlds. He studied the Force in all its guises throughout the galaxy, whether it was the shamanism of Jarvashqiine or the tales of the Tyia. Coupled with perversions of the secrets he ripped from the living minds of Jedi he captured during the Purge, he learned more than he ever expected.

One such victim was Ashka Boda, possessor of the famed Jedi Holocron itself. With this artifact in his grasp, he had little need for any more living Jedi, save as pupils.

He sifted this lore till he could find every secret he needed to continue his studies. He had long ago gone beyond any knowledge to be found in the recovered teachings of the Krath or the Heresiarchs. Since then, his studies had principally been experimental. He gathered this knowledge, mostly crude and simplistic variations on traditional Jedi teachings, into a great assemblage of Dark Side Lore. He completed two volumes in this Dark Side Compendium: *The Book of Anger* and *The Weakness of Inferiors*.

The Emperor's third volume, *The Creation of Monsters,* is still in manuscript. Prior to his death above the Pinnacle Moon, the Emperor had planned *hundreds* of additional volumes. With the immortality his clone tanks provided him, he thought he literally had all the time in the universe with which to probe the limits of the Force.

The Book Of Anger

Emperor Palpatine's first volume deals with the use of emotion to control the Force. He considers *anger* to be the most potent emotional form. With anger, the Jedi can call upon the Dark Side, harnessing it for great power and destruction. Palpatine teaches that anger and rage, mixed with intelligent control, call upon the Dark Side with a very fine level of control, and can even kill from a great distance.

The Weakness of Inferiors

This second book teaches control, without violence, over the innocent, the ignorant, and "all inferiors."

Palpatine's main philosophy is quoted below:

1) ALL POWER COMES FROM OUTSIDE THE WEAK. The weak have *never* been known to believe in themselves or in their ability to wield power.

2) THE FACE OF AUTHORITY. The weak live as in a dream. All their thoughts, actions, and urges are governed by the face and the voice that controls this dream. The face and voice they have learned to obey. The face and voice of *Authority*.

3) THE LAW OF FEAR. A consequence of the first two tenets is that the weak live in *fear*. The mere *suggestion of violence* from one in authority is enough to inspire their obedience. How can one who doesn't believe in his own powers stand against the power of another? It is impossible.

4) THE WEAK DO NOT UNDERSTAND THE FORCE. The Force is the ultimate means to gain authority over the weak. The weak do not understand the Force. The weak do not sense the Force, therefore how can they understand or use the Force? So it is that the weak are at the mercy of those who know and use the power of the Force. The proper use of the Force can inspire awe and obedience in the weak.

It has been said that *anyone* who knows the ways of the Force can set himself up as a King on any world where only he knows the ways of the Force. *Any* Jedi could do this. But the Jedi, fools

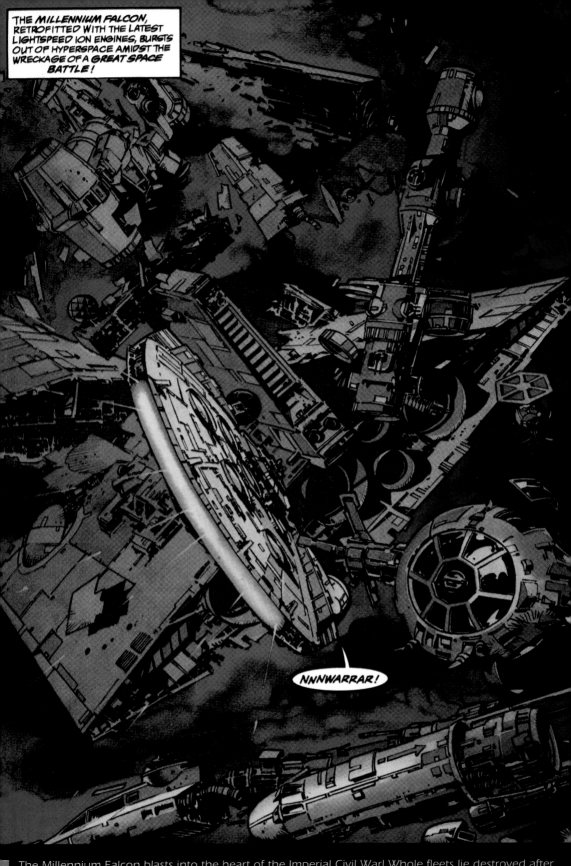

The Millennium Falcon blasts into the heart of the Imperial Civil War! Whole fleets lie destroyed after countless battles for Coruscant. Art by Cam Kennedy.

THE RAVAGES OF CIVIL WAR! MUTINOUS IMPERIALS ARE DEADLOCKED WITH FORCES LOYAL TO THE EMPEROR'S INNER CIRCLE FOR POSSESSION OF A WORLD THAT ONCE RULED AN EMPIRE!

The Siege of Imperial City. Coruscant, once the gleaming capital of the Republic, is now a ravaged battleground. In the foreground, forces from one of the Imperial factions dig in. Midground, a destroyed TIE Tank, also known as a Century Tank. Background, an Arakyd WR-85 Tank Droid, first of a new line

Dark Empire, Issue #2. Art by Dave Dorman.

" WHEN THE EMPEROR CREATED THE *DEATH STAR*, CALAMARI WAS AT THE TOP OF THE LIST OF WORLDS SCHEDULED TO BE *ANNIHILATED* BY THAT DREADFUL BATTLE-STATION ...

"...AND NOW, AT LAST, WHOEVER IS REUNIFYING THE EMPIRE IS CARRYING OUT THE EMPEROR'S DECISION TO DISCIPLINE US ... WITH THESE NEW *WORLD DEVASTATORS*!

Dark Empire, Issue #3. Art by Dave Dorman.

The Rebel Star Destroyer Emancipator pierces the Imperial fleet during the Battle of Calamari. X-wing fighters provide escort for the new V-wing speeder transports, each carrying four V-wing airspeeders into battle. Art by Cam Kennedy.

Nar Shaddaa, the smugglers' moon. Once a center of galactic trade, this moon is now a center of intergalactic crime. It is here that Han Solo has come for only his friends Shug Ninx and Salla Zend can help save Luke Skywalker from the clutches of the Dark Side. Art by Cam Kennedy.

Dark Empire, Issue #4. Art by Dave Dorman.

The Imperial Freight complex, the terminal for thousands of cargo haulers in the employ of the Empire

The Eclipse, the Emperor's devastating flagship Super Star Destroyer. Black as death, the monstrous

Palpatine faces final defeat as the power of his Force storm turns against him. The storm consumes his flagship Eclipse as Luke and Leia rush to safety. Art by Cam Kennedy.

STAR WARS

that they are, adhere to a religion in which the Force is used only in the service of others.

How shortsighted of them. Is that not why they lost the Galaxy to the Dark Side?

In these cantos and the hundreds of thousands that follow, it is apparent that the Emperor has plumbed depths of darkness unknown before. Whether he has done so out of a need to achieve knowledge, or whether he has been *drawn* thus far is unknown and perhaps unknowable. What is known is that the Emperor gathered all the greatest lore of the Dark Side and collected it. This cost him greatly, as the Dark Side consumes its servants even as its followers consume each other.

Dark Side Adepts

At the height of the New Order, long before the Rebellion gained its first victories, Palpatine would vacation on Byss and entertain his circle of intimates. Beings of great intelligence, they had proven their loyalty to their master. Guests at the palace were soon indoctrinated into the ways of the Dark Side.

Unlike many of the Emperor's other servants, a number of these were aliens. Most of these individuals had already mastered the unique sorceries of their own species, and the Emperor has brought them to Byss as much to study their knowledge as to train them in his.

While none of them were permitted to advance far compared to Palpatine's own level of power, they did become quite powerful indeed. Some were taught ways of combat and made into Dark Jedi. Others joined the elite of Imperial functionaries, traversing the galaxy and seeing to the proper enforcement of Palpatine's decrees. Still others were courtiers at the Palace in the new capital on Byss.

Whatever they do, they enact the Emperor's will and policies with his total trust and confidence because their link to him through the Force allows him to always observe them. Before the Emperor's defeat, many had been gathered into the Imperial Ruling Council. It had been planned that eventually these adepts would replace the system of Moffs, Grand Moffs and governors, instituting a Dark Side Theocracy. With his adepts securely in power, they were to participate in experiments on the "Science of Darkness," feeding on and draining the life essence of the citizenry.

■ Gwellib Ap-Llewff
Type: Dark Side Adept
DEXTERITY 3D
Blaster 7D, bows 7D+1, brawling parry 6D+1, dodge 6D+2, lightsaber 9D+2, melee combat 7D+1, melee parry 8D

On The Origin Of Force Storms

"I have learned that *Anger* and *Will,* joined together, are the greatest Power.

"I have learned to meditate upon Anger and Will with clarity and precision, and I have learned to open the hidden reservoirs of Dark Side Power.

"Anger concentrated by Will in the vital center of the body creates a portal through which vast energies are released — the energies of the Dark Side of the Force.

"Standing watch with the mind, in my meditation of Anger, I have slain my enemies from great distances, through the Dark Side Power that permeates the Galaxy. I have created lightning, and unleashed its destructive fire.

"Using this knowledge, I can unleash the Dark Side energies that are all around us, even to shatter the fabric of space itself. In this way, I have created storms."

— Palpatine
From *The Book of Anger*

LET IT BE HIS *"FREE CHOICE,"* IF THAT'S WHAT HE WANTS TO BELIEVE...

...BUT HE'S WALKING TO HIS *DOOM!*

■ Dark Side Adepts in the service of the Emperor. Savuud Thimram (right) and Gwellib Ap-Llewff (left) discuss Luke Skywalker's fate.

KNOWLEDGE 4D+2
Bureaucracy 6D, cultures 5D, intimidation 7D, languages 6D, planetary systems 5D, scholar: Dark Side Lore 6D+1, streetwise 5D, survival 6D, willpower 5D+2
MECHANICAL 2D
Beast riding 5D, repulsorlift operation 4D+1
PERCEPTION 3D+1
Command 5D, persuasion 4D, search 4D+1
STRENGTH 2D+2
Brawling 5D, climbing/jumping 5D, lifting 6D, stamina 9D
TECHNICAL 2D+1
Security 5D
Special Abilities:
Force Skills: Control 7D+1, sense 9D+1, alter 8D
Control: Accelerate healing, control pain, enhance attribute*, resist stun
Sense: Combat sense*, danger sense*, life detection, life sense
Alter: Telekinesis
Control and Sense: Lightsaber combat
Control and Alter: Feed on Dark Side**, inflict pain*
Control, Sense and Alter: Affect mind, enhanced coordination*
* Described in the *Dark Force Rising Sourcebook*
** Described in *Galaxy Guide 9: Fragments From The Rim*
This character is Force-sensitive.
Force Points: 9
Dark Side Points: 8
Character Points: 13
Move: 10
Equipment: Lightsaber (5D damage), ceremonial jewel-encrusted walking stick, ceremonial dress from native world

■ Savuud Thimram

Type: Dark Side Adept
DEXTERITY 3D
Dodge 4D, melee combat 5D+2, melee parry 5D
KNOWLEDGE 3D+2
Alien species 5D+2, bureaucracy 6D+2, cultures 6D, languages 7D+1, planetary systems 6D, scholar: Dark Side Lore 6D+1, scholar: exotic poisons 8D+1
MECHANICAL 2D
PERCEPTION 3D+1
Bargain 5D, command 5D+1, con 5D, gambling 4D, persuasion 7D+1
STRENGTH 2D+2
Swimming 5D
TECHNICAL 2D+1
First aid 8D, security 6D
Special Abilities:
Force Skills: Control 8D, sense 5D+2, alter 8D+1
Control: Accelerate healing, control pain, detoxify poison*, emptiness, reduce injury
Sense: Danger sense*, life detection, life sense, receptive telepathy
Alter: Injure/kill, telekinesis
Control and Sense: Lightsaber combat
Control and Alter: Inflict pain*
Control, Sense and Alter: Affect mind, telekinetic kill*
* Described in the *Dark Force Rising Sourcebook*.
This character is Force-sensitive.
Force Points: 2
Dark Side Points: 19
Character Points: 5
Move: 10
Equipment: Blast armor (+1D physical, +2 energy), robes

Imperial Sovereign Protectors

This most elite order of the Emperor's bodyguards is selected from the main body of the crimson-robed Royal Guard. They are stationed in small groups throughout the Empire as watchmen over all the palaces and monasteries that Palpatine haunts, as well as guarding the Emperor.

No other group of soldiers in the entire galaxy, Empire or Republic, is as highly trained or motivated. They have an awesome responsibility. With Palpatine's knowledge of the Force, and with the importance of his projects at the Clone Vats on Byss, these armored figures have the most important duty in the entire New Order. Each of them is clothed in lightweight, yet elaborate ceremonial armor, and armed with unique and exotic weapons. They are experts at armed and unarmed combat.

One reason the Emperor created the Sovereign Protectors was because he thought it unwise to limit the aspirations of his followers. By setting nearly unattainable goals and watching his men struggle to achieve them, he can keep them under better control. By creating higher and higher circles of elite status, it motivates them all to push themselves constantly.

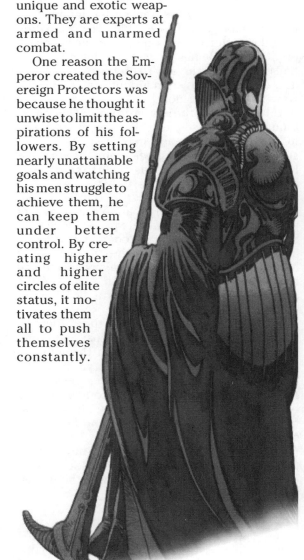

Just as the Royal Guard are the finest of the Imperial stormtroopers, so the Protectors are the highest order yet. Palpatine may create still more elevated ranks in the future, but for now, the Protectors are the summit.

The training and testing procedure that each Protector undergoes is elaborate and time consuming; it may take years to qualify, and the waiting list is enormous. Part of the selection process is based on traditional combat fitness, including tests of stamina, strength, dexterity, and the ability to endure pain. Other tests include mental acuity, reaction time, loyalty, intelligence. Once they have shown exemplary achievement in all these matters, the most crucial step is begun. Unlike all the other soldiers at the Emperor's command, the Sovereign Protectors are taught in the ways of the Dark Side.

Tutored in the Force by the Senior Dark Side Adepts in the Emperor's service, they are taught only elementary skills, so they must always be subservient. And subservient they are — so utterly unswerving in their loyalty that it is said that they can't even perceive any thing which might corrupt them from their service; others say they would kill themselves in an instant if ordered to by their Master. Whether true or not, that unthinking loyalty will be most useful to them later because those who distinguish themselves here are sometimes selected to become Dark Jedi themselves.

■ Imperial Sovereign Protectors

Type: Imperial Sovereign Protectors
DEXTERITY 5D
Archaic guns 8D, blaster 9D, blaster artillery 6D+2, bows 6D, brawling parry 7D+2, dodge 8D, melee combat 6D+2, melee parry 6D, missile weapons 7D, thrown weapons 6D+1, vehicle blasters 6D+2
KNOWLEDGE 4D
Intimidation 6D+1, law enforcement 5D+2, scholar: Dark Side lore 5D, streetwise 5D, survival 7D, willpower 5D+2
MECHANICAL 3D+2
Beast riding 5D
PERCEPTION 4D+1
Command 5D, search 6D, sneak 5D
STRENGTH 3D
Brawling 6D, climbing/jumping 7D, lifting 4D, stamina 6D
TECHNICAL 3D
Demolition 5D, security 7D
Special Abilities:
Force Skills: Control 2D, sense 1D, alter 1D
Force Powers:
Control: Remain conscious, resist stun
Sense: Combat sense*, danger sense*, life detection, life sense, sense Force
Alter: Injure/kill
*Described in the *Dark Force Rising Sourcebook*.
This character is Force-sensitive.
Force Points: 1
Dark Side Points: 3
Character Points: 9
Move: 11
Equipment: Force pike (STR+3D damage), battle armor (+3D physical, +2D energy, sensor suite adds +1D to *search* or *Perception*)

Imperial Sentinels

These mute titans are the subject of endless talk among those at the court; their origin is unknown. While obviously inhuman, their intricately wrapped bodies and draping garments are something out of a forgotten legend.

Even the Imperial Sovereign Protectors have no idea, nor real interest, in their origin. An outsider might assume some confusion would occur as to responsibilities, but no interference ever occurs because nothing is done without the Emperor's direct order. Ordinarily, the Sentinels function primarily as guardians for the Dark Side Adepts that do the Emperor's bidding.

The first Sentinels appeared, typically, without any explanation, at the scene of a battle where a few Jedi had been captured. Bearing cryptic but authentic datachips, they assumed complete control over the disposition of a particular prisoner. Escorting him back on a dungeon ship, they formed a sort of praetorian guard for Ashka Boda as he journeyed to Coruscant and his doom.

As in the case of the Imperial Grand Vizier, idle rumor and speculation sprung up to answer questions not asked aloud. Some suggest the Sentinels are from some captured race of giants, enslaved to serve the Emperor. Some believe the Sentinels are immense droids or cyborgs. Still others whisper the Dark Side Adepts are somehow behind these aberrations. Little do these whisperers realize just how close to the truth they may be.

The Sentinels are clones, mutated by the Dark Side Adepts as part of their training. During the growth cycle, odd chemicals that suppress the growth of higher brain functions are introduced. Simultaneously, the Adepts attempt to form a mental link to them. If the process is successful, the Sentinels end up as automatons: living statues dependent on the will of the Adepts themselves for purpose or movement. If the process is unsuccessful, the living monstrosities are disposed of.

For the duration of the wretched being's existence, it is the slave of the Dark Side Adept, knowing no other will than the Adept's.

■ Imperial Sentinels

Type: Imperial Sentinels
DEXTERITY 5D
Blaster 6D, brawling parry 8D, dodge 7D, melee combat 8D, melee parry 8D
KNOWLEDGE 0D
MECHANICAL 0D
Beast riding 4D
PERCEPTION 2D
Search 5D, sneak 4D
STRENGTH 5D
Brawling 6D, climbing/jumping 8D, lifting 9D, stamina 8D
TECHNICAL 0D

Security 4D
Move: 11
Equipment: Battle armor (adds +2D physical, +1D energy, -1D to *Dexterity* and all related skills), forceaxe (STR+3D+2 damage)
Note: Imperial Sentinels are completely dependent upon Adepts for will. They have no ability to think for themselves — they can only do what they are told. It is believed that the Dark Side Adepts can perceive what the Sentinel's perceive, thus allowing them to maintain complete control, but this rumor has never been verified.

New Force Powers

Control

Rage

Control Difficulty: Difficult
Required Power: *Hibernation trance*
Warning: A Jedi who uses this power gains a Dark Side Point.
Note: This power can only be used by characters who have been consumed by the Dark Side of the Force.
Effect: This power allows a character to feel the dread influence of the Dark Side. It functions as a counterpart to *emptiness*.

The character must tense herself completely, and allow the mindless rage of the Dark Side to possess her. When using this power, a character will appear lifeless. They are amplifying the negative aspects of their own personality, leaving the face clenched in a rictus of horror and fear.

A character must determine how long she wishes to be in *rage* when she enters the trance. Barring an attack or the arrival of a specific person (as explained below), the Jedi will stay in the trance for the chosen duration. The Jedi must make a Difficult *control* roll for every four hours in the trance or she will come out of the trance.

When the Jedi leaves this state, she gets a +10 modifier to all Force skill rolls for a period of time equal to the time spent in *rage*. The character takes one die of damage for every two hours they were in the trance after the bonus has subsided.

Like *emptiness,* this power makes characters oblivious to their surroundings; they cannot move. Unlike *emptiness*, however, characters in this state strongly exude the Dark Side. The internal focusing does provide some protection for the character against others using the Force on them. Add the *rage control* roll to the difficulty roll when another attempts to use a Force power on someone in *rage*.

Characters dehydrate and hunger twice as fast normally when using *rage* and are even more susceptible to damage (-1D to *Strength* to resist damage from physical and energy attacks while in this state). Characters who plan on an extended trance will need intravenous nourishment.

In *rage*, the character is less oblivious to her surroundings than a corresponding Jedi in *emptiness*. For example, any physical contact by a living being may revive them (the Jedi must make a Moderate *control* roll) and provoke an instant berserker-like attack, regardless of who the person may be. The character must then make a Difficult *control* roll to cease the attack before the offending character has been killed.

A character using *rage* can choose to anticipate the arrival of a foe. They must make a Difficult *sense* roll (modified by relationship) with the *life sense* power at the time they enter *rage*. This will allow them to instantly awaken (Easy *control* roll) if the expected person comes within five meters of the person in *rage*.

Example: *While preparing to transfer his life to a new clone body, Palpatine expects an attack from Luke Skywalker. When he enters rage, he must also make a Difficult sense roll using the life sense power to anticipate Luke entering the Clone Chamber. The difficulty is 20, +7 for relationship (they are acquaintances) to equal 27, plus Palpatine suffers a penalty for having to make two skill uses in one round: the sense roll for life sense and the control roll for rage. Palpatine's roll is 44, so when Luke enters the chamber, Palpatine instantly*

wakes from his rage *and confronts Luke ...*

This power may be used in a preparation ritual for the *transfer life* power. When a *raged* person uses *transfer life,* their original body is instantly and totally consumed by the Dark Side, often bursting into unholy blue flames. For every three points by which the *control* roll exceeded the *rage* difficulty, the body does 1D damage upon explosion (three meter blast radius).

Example: *Palpatine, while confronting Luke in the Clone Chamber, has been in* rage *for three hours, gaining +10 to all his Force skills. Palpatine's difficulty roll was 20. He rolled a 35. He successfully uses the* transfer life *power and his old body explodes in a 5D damage burst of flame.*

Control, Sense And Alter Powers

Create Force Storms

"The ability to destroy a planet is insignificant compared to the power of the Force."
— Darth Vader

Control Difficulty: Heroic
Sense Difficulty: Heroic
Alter Difficulty: Heroic. Modified by proximity. Modified by size of storm desired: +5 for 100 meters or less, +10 for 100 meters to one kilometer, +15 for a base of one kilometer, and +2 to difficulty for every kilometer diameter in size. Modified by damage: +5 per 1D of damage. Must make Heroic rolls each successive round to control the storm. Must make a Very Difficult role to dissipate the storm.

Required Powers: *Hibernation trance, life detection, life sense, magnify senses, receptive telepathy, sense Force, telekinesis, farseeing* (see *Dark Force Rising Sourcebook*), *projective telepathy, instinctive astrogation* (see *Galaxy Guide 9: Fragments From The Rim*), *rage*

Warning: Force Storms are immensely destructive and violate the laws of nature. A Jedi using this power automatically gains a Dark Side Point.

Effect: This is perhaps the single most destructive Force power known. This power allows the Jedi to twist the space-time continuum to create vast storms of force. The power also allows limited control of these storms. Capable of creating annihilating vortices, the storms can swallow whole fleets of spaceships or tear the surfaces off worlds.

Use of this power requires the focusing of hate and anger to an almost palpable degree and there is considerable danger involved. Some are

able to create Force storms, but fail at harnessing what they have foolishly unleashed. Often, those who fail to control the storm are themselves consumed and destroyed. If the user is destroyed, the storm dissipates within minutes.

When the Force user attempts to create a Force storm, the Jedi must determine the diameter and the amount of damage (the damage dice are capital scale). If the Jedi fails any of the rolls, the storm is summoned with the desired damage, but it attempts to consume the summoner. The summoner can attempt unusual maneuvers with the storm, such as to create a vortex to draw unwary victims to a specified point, at a +10 to difficulty.

Doppleganger

Control Difficulty: Very Difficult
Sense Difficulty: Very Difficult
Alter Difficulty: Heroic
Required Powers: *Control pain, emptiness, life detection, life sense, magnify senses, receptive telepathy, sense Force, telekinesis, projective telepathy, control another's pain, transfer Force, affect mind, dim other's senses*
This power must be kept "up."
Warning: A character who uses this power receives a Dark Side Point.
Time To Use: Five minutes
Effect: This power creates a doppleganger of the person using the power. The doppleganger is an illusion, but to those who interact with it, it will seem real. The user can sense all normal senses through the doppleganger, and the duplicate seems to have form and substance: the doppleganger registers as normal on all droid audio and video sensors. Those who are with the doppleganger believe it to be a real person. The doppleganger acts with half the skill dice of the person using the power. The user must roll once every five minutes to maintain the doppleganger; if the Jedi stops using the power or the doppleganger is fatally injured, it simply fades away.

Force Harmony

Control Difficulty: Difficult, modified by proximity
Sense Difficulty: Difficult, modified by relationship
Alter Difficulty: Moderate
Required Power: *Life detection, life sense, projective telepathy, receptive telepathy*
This power can be kept "up."
Effect: This allows several willing Jedi to manifest the power of the Light Side. As long as this power is held up, it bathes the users in the celestial illumination that is the Light Side. It can

act as a shield against the powers of the Dark Side, giving an extra 5D for each Force user involved to resist the effects of powers called upon by Dark Side servants. Note that +5D may appear to be an immense bonus, but since this power must be kept up, the Jedi calling upon the power is suffering a 2D penalty simply for calling upon this power. One can only link as many Force users as the initiator of the power has *control* or *sense* dice, whichever skill is lower. For example, if Leia used *Force harmony*, since her *control* is 5D+1 and her *sense* is 4D+2, she would only be able to link a total of four people (including herself).

When acting as a shield against the Dark Side, if both the *control* and *sense* rolls exceed the success roll of the Dark Side power used (if the power requires multiple skill rolls, the highest roll), then the Dark Side power is interrupted. All "up" powers are interrupted as if the user were stunned. It does not cancel out the presence of the Dark Side, but can distract its servants and make their actions more difficult.

Example: *Leia and Luke Skywalker try to disrupt Palpatine's Force storm, which is destroying the Republic's fleet. Palpatine is in the room with them.*

Luke and Leia and Leia's new child are related by blood and are all strong with the Force. Leia spends a Force Point and links Luke and the child with the Light Side; her control roll is 47 and her sense roll is 36. She successfully uses the Force harmony power, giving everyone a +5D against the effects of any Dark Side powers.

If both of these rolls exceed Palpatine's highest skill roll when he summoned the Force storm, then Palpatine's control over the Force storm is severed.

Drain Life Essence

Control Difficulty: Very Difficult, inversely modified by relationship. For example, using this power on a close relative would add +30 to the difficulty; using this power on complete strangers of other species would add nothing to the difficulty.

Sense Difficulty: Use the chart below:

Difficulty	Number of Victims
Very Easy	1-5
Easy	6-50
Moderate	51-1,000
Difficult	1,001-50,000
Very Difficult	50,001-1 million
Heroic	1 million to 10 million

Alter Difficulty: Easy for willing, worshipful subjects. Difficult for ambivalent or apathetic individuals. Heroic for enemies. Add +10 to the difficulty if individuals are imbued with the Light Side of the Force.

Required Power: *Control pain, hibernation trance, life detection, life sense, magnify senses, receptive telepathy, sense Force, telekinesis, far-seeing*, projective telepathy, control another's pain*, transfer Force, affect mind, control mind*, dim other's senses*

*Described in Dark Force Rising Sourcebook. This power may be kept "up."

Warning: Any Jedi who uses this power gains a Dark Side Point.

Effect: This power allows a Jedi to draw life energy from those around him and to channel the negative effects of the Dark Side into those victims.

All living things are a part of and contribute to the Force; even those with no awareness of the Force are affected by and are a part of it. Many beings go through their daily lives wasting much of their life energy. This power draws that life energy from beings, allowing a Jedi to use that energy to further his or her own ends.

In order to draw this energy, the Jedi must roll for this power once per day; this power is considered "up" at all times, and thus the Jedi suffers appropriate die penalties.

The amount of energy the Jedi draws depends on the number of individuals affected by the power and how long they have been drained.

For individuals who have been drained for less then one week or longer than one month:

1-5—One Force Point per week
6-50—One Force Point per five days
51-1,000—One Force Point per three days
1,001-50,000—One Force Point per two days
50,001-1 million—One Force Point per day
1 million to 10 million—One Force Point per 12 hours

For individuals who have been drained longer than one week and less than one month:

1-5—One Force Point per five days and +1D to all Force skills
6-50—One Force Point per three days and +2D to all Force skills
51-1,000—One Force Point per two days and +3D to all Force skills
1,001-50,000—One Force Point per day and +3D+2 to all Force skills
50,001-1 million—One Force Point per 12 hours and +4D to all Force skills
1 million to 10 million—One Force Point per 6 hours and +4D+2 to all Force skills

Transfer Life

Control Difficulty: Heroic, modified by relationship. If target is unwilling, increase difficulty by +15.

Sense Difficulty: Heroic, modified by proximity. If target is unwilling, increase difficulty by +15.

Alter Difficulty: Variable, depending on willingness and Force affinity.

Circumstances	Difficulty
Specially Prepared Clone Host Body	Easy
Recently Dead Body	Moderate
Live Willing Host	Very Difficult
Live Unwilling Host	Heroic

Those who are Force-sensitive may make an opposed *alter* or *willpower* roll, selecting either the roll or the difficulty, whichever is higher.

Required Powers: *Absorb/dissipate energy, accelerate healing, control pain, detoxify poison*, emptiness, hibernation trance, reduce injury, remain conscious, resist stun, life detection, life sense, magnify senses, receptive telepathy, sense Force, injure/kill, telekinesis, farseeing*, projective telepathy, accelerate another's heal-ing, control another's pain*, feed on Dark Side**, inflict pain*, return another to consciousness, transfer Force, affect mind, control mind*, dim other's senses*

* Described in the *Dark Force Rising Sourcebook*

** Described in *Galaxy Guide 9: Fragments from the Rim*

Warning: Any Jedi using this power receives two Dark Side Points. If attempting to possess an unwilling host, the Jedi receives four Dark Side Points.

Effect: This power allows the character to transfer his or her life energy into another body. The key to immortality itself, this is one of the most difficult and evil of all Dark Side powers. To overcome a spirit already residing in a body is nearly impossible. This is why the power is nearly useless without the ability to clone host bodies.

Though theoretically possible, it is not yet known what the effect on an unborn fetus would be. Fortunately, there is almost no history of this power being used successfully. It is believed that if the user's body perishes as an attempt fails, the user's life energy is lost, dispersed to the void.

■ Chapter Five
Planets

Overview

A galaxy is an enormous place indeed, with hundreds of billions of stars. How many habitable worlds might there be? How many civilizations might arise on them? Imagine the complexity and staggering difficulty of uniting so many worlds into a single government. Still, with determination, this was achieved and the Old Republic ruled for 25,000 years.

Despite ages of progress and justice, eventually the Republic weakened and fell due to internal corruption and civic apathy. Replaced with the Galactic Empire, the Republic's delicate balancing act to guarantee freedom and opportunity for all was ignored in favor of a simpler solution: rule by fear. Understandably, there have been those who opposed this; these people were the members of the Rebel Alliance. After many years of conflict, the Rebel Alliance finally dealt a staggering blow to the galaxy's oppressors.

The Empire ruled despotically for years, but it ruled a united galaxy. The galaxy is united no more. Initially successful in restoring freedom to three quarters of the former Empire, the New Republic seemed a thriving government. Recently, the Empire, through Grand Admiral Thrawn, struck back. Now, the lines of battle are roughly drawn with half the galaxy in Imperial hands and half under the control of the New Republic.

With the multiple shifts of power over the years, the front lines have shifted many times. Currently, the New Republic has a stable hold on many of the worlds in the Expansion Region, the Colonies Region and several other key regions of the galaxy. It also has control of many less vital regions (less vital in that they are not key to the overall strategy of maintaining control of the galaxy; many of these regions do make substantial contributions of raw materials, soldiers and other important supplies). Unable to hold onto Coruscant, the Rebel Alliance has made strategic withdrawals to their current command base in the Da Soocha system.

The Empire has regained the Core Worlds, and still holds the Deep Galactic Core, as well as many high industry regions beyond the Core Worlds. It seemed that the Imperial Coalition was dispersed — while it held Coruscant, the former capital wasn't used as the prime base of operations.

The Empire supplies its fleets from power bases in the Mid-Rim and the reclaimed Inner Rim, where the industrial planets depend on wartime economies to survive. However, the most significant Imperial victory occurred when the Empire retook the Core Worlds, linking Imperial holdings all the way to Wild Space. Once control of these vital planets was ensured, the Empire began bulwarking them against further attack.

As Palpatine's plan unfolded, the Empire launched strikes deep into the heart of Mon Calamari space. If successful, these strikes would have cut the Republic in half. Fortunately for the Republic, this strategy failed.

When Palpatine returned, the Deep Core planet of Byss served as the Empire's capital. With the chaos following Palpatine's death, the Empire seems disorganized and confused, and thus its strategy is difficult to determine.

Because of the lack of a centralized government and the continuing conflict over the past six years, many systems have grouped together and formed protective federations, notably the Dawferm Selfhood States and the Botor Enclave. Some individual worlds, like Lianna in the Tion, have instituted home rule. Many worlds and groups have declared themselves neutral in the continuing conflict. The Corporate Sector Authority, with control of a vast volume of space, is the largest of these neutral states and has been selling weapons to any group with ready cash.

The Imperial Hyperspace Security Net

The nature of hyperdrive allows a great deal of stealth in battle. Ships with precise enough calculations can appear in realspace without warning, to devastating effect. Enemy ships caught by surprise might be destroyed before they even realize they are under attack.

Alliance General Jan Dodonna perfected modern tactics of hit and run skirmishes through careful use of the hyperdrive. Often vastly outnumbered and without resources for sustained engagements, it was a perfect match of need and opportunity. The Rebel ships would emerge in realspace, make a quick assault and then return to hyperspace before Imperial reinforcements could be brought in to eliminate the Rebel ships. This mainstay of Rebel tactics forced the Empire to stop sending out unarmed convoys. Admiral Ackbar enhanced the technique, striking deep into enemy space with a feint to draw out

Imperial escort vessels. Once the bait had been taken, a secondary force attacked or captured the now undefended prime objective.

On a larger scale, whole fleets can surprise planets in full-scale assaults. Since planetary shields and ion cannon take time to ready for combat, enemy fleets could devastate key locations on a planet before its defenses could be brought to bear. The Imperial Hyperspace Security Net is an attempt to give planets, and with further technological refinements, starships, advance warning of ships approaching in hyperspace.

The first ingredient of the Net is a known technology, that of the artificial gravity shadow. Each mass in realspace projects a mass shadow in hyperspace. Ships in hyperspace are destroyed if they pass through a mass shadow, and thus all ships are equipped with advanced sensors that cut out a ship's hyperdrive if it travels too close to a mass shadow.

This technology was developed after an acci-

dental discovery in the Sedri system. Here, the Empire discovered that it was possible to generate an *artificial* gravity well. The mission there was foiled by Rebel agents, but Imperial scientists learned much. After many months of research, these scientists learned how to create an artificial gravity well. These gravity well generators were mounted in the newly constructed *Interdictor*-class cruisers. They proved quite reliable under limited circumstances. The Interdictors had a dual function. They could force a ship from hyperspace and they could prevent a ship in realspace from jumping to hyperspace, thus preventing escape in hit and run assaults. The introduction of the Interdictors forced the Rebel Alliance to be more cautious in its attacks on Imperial shipping.

The second ingredient of the Net is the ability to detect incoming starships. Using technology developed for the HoloNet, the Security Net is a system of connected non-mass transceivers linked by a network of coordinated hyperspace S-threads. The HoloNet's transceivers are programmed to pass communications in specific frequencies. The Security Net's transceivers project cross-channeled radiation. When a ship in hyperspace passes through this radiation, it registers a disturbance in hyperspace that the transceivers can detect at fairly short distances (cosmically speaking). Once a ship is detected, the gravity well generators can be used to force a ship back to realspace.

This can serve as a limited early detection system. Unfortunately, the technology is so bulky and expensive that a Net is only practical under very specific conditions. They can be built around systems, but realistically they can only cover the most common hyperspace entry routes; even this type of Net would still have many "holes" in it, allowing ships using experimental routes to pass through undetected. The technology of the Security Net has been made more practical by equipping the transceivers with hyperdrive engines and nav computers. The transceivers then randomly jump from point to point, allowing the Net to cover many more locations. If incoming ships are unaware of the jump pattern of the transceivers, ships can find it very difficult to slip through the Net.

Often, a system using a Security Net rounds out its security with patrol vessels, Interdictor cruisers, asteroid mines, anti-matter particles and probe droids to discourage unwanted travelers.

The Deep Core

The peripheral sphere of the galactic core has long served as the seat of civilization for the

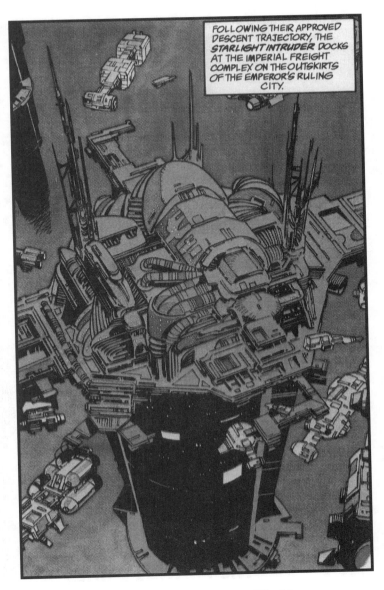

FOLLOWING THEIR APPROVED DESCENT TRAJECTORY, THE *STARLIGHT INTRUDER* DOCKS AT THE IMPERIAL FREIGHT COMPLEX ON THE OUTSKIRTS OF THE EMPEROR'S RULING CITY.

Old Republic and was called the Core Worlds. The Deep Core, at the heart of the galaxy, had resisted most exploration. The Deep Core is filled with a myriad of blazing suns, some within a few light hours of each other. The closeness of these stars has long proved a nearly insurmountable navigational hurdle.

Only the single-mindedness of a tyrant like Palpatine could pierce the final veil of this untouched region. Even before his ascension to the presidency, he had funded and promoted long range Deep Core explorations. He ordered the launch of thousands of probots programmed to chart safe hyperspace routes into and through the Deep Core. It took years, but three probe droids succeeded. By this time, Palpatine had assumed the throne.

Modified scout ships were launched into the Deep Core. Survey teams catalogued and surveyed hundreds of potentially habitable worlds. However, no heroes' welcome faced the returning scouts. Palpatine ordered them put to death, ensuring that the paths into the Deep Core would remain a guarded secret.

Over the next few decades, Palpatine sponsored the selected colonization of a few choice worlds in the Deep Core. Here was his stronghold of loyalty, replete with secret military facilities, shipyards and training grounds for his exclusive troops, worlds of loyal servants and private retreats for him and his select ministers. Over many years, rumors of secret Deep Core colonies had surfaced, but they were never given more credibility than tales of lost space fleets, giant space slugs and dark magicians ruling empires out in Wild Space. The Deep Core retained its aura of mystery — only a few million of Palpatine's most loyal supporters knew the truth.

Palpatine was able to maintain his veil of secrecy due to the inaccessibility of the Deep Core. As he prepared his return to the war against the Rebellion, he needed to bring supplies and troops into the Deep Core. Selected Deep Core haulers were given appropriate coordinates into the Core — all the paths were marked by the Security Net. Aside from those few known paths, it is virtually impossible to navigate a path into the Deep Core; while it is entirely possible that there are many other paths into the region, the odds of finding one through exploration are very low. Palpatine ordered many of the navigable regions mined, patrolled and otherwise blockaded to further prevent unauthorized exploration.

The Fortress Worlds

Deprived of the security of the Deep Core, it seemed increasingly apparent that even the worlds of the Inner systems and Core might someday be "liberated" by the New Republic. Many worlds eagerly threw off the yoke of despotism, but those in power had a vested interest in seeing the Empire endure. As battle lines raced closer and closer to the all-important Imperial System itself, lords, nobles and governors had little recourse but to leave before being overrun.

In short order, Coruscant, Alsakan, Grizmallt, Wukkar and a host of the most heavily populated worlds surrendered to Admiral Ackbar's fleet. Without delay, the New Republic established its capital on Coruscant and the long process of de-imperialization began. The process was difficult since many New Order sup-

porters feigned loyalty to the New Republic. The new government, noble in its intentions, was riddled with Imperial holdouts. Still, the Republic moved on, bringing freedom to many worlds.

With the arrival of Grand Admiral Thrawn, the balance of strength changed seemingly overnight. The Alliance retreat was considerably more orderly, though no less desperate. While defensive actions held off the main fleet, Republic transports raised ship. A formal ceremony to reconsecrate the capitol city earned General Balan fame throughout Imperial space and a triumphal parade, but did little to reassure newly reinstalled nobles of their position. More drastic measures were necessary to guarantee their control over these worlds.

As the Mutiny seemed more imminent, various commanders set out to fortify their worlds. The so-called "Fortress Worlds" were established. Planetary shields were a prime method. More powerful and larger than those used by the Rebels on Hoth, they were enormous energy screens that wrapped entire planets with a protective force field, deflecting bombardment and blocking any landing attempt.

To further augment these shields, governors summoned their fleets, sometimes in the midst of battle, to form perimeter defense squadrons in the system. Able to respond instantly to any incursion, the fleets were an overpowering border guard. Depending on the strategic importance of the system, the size of the fleet might vary from thirty ships for Gyndine, to hundreds for Aargau. Strongly sectarian, it wasn't uncommon for fleets to refuse aid to neighboring sectors under attack.

Still, this was not enough in some cases, and those with the wealth to indulge their paranoia invested in exotic armaments. Airless moons bristled with turbolaser and ion cannon emplacements, asteroid belts were mined with anti-matter particles and reflecting satellite arrays for surface based beams. Indeed, many of the Fortress Worlds could hold off an attack for months, or years if necessary.

Byss

Byss was the secret capital of the Emperor's revived Empire. It is a mythic world, bathed in the Dark Side of the Force, in the heart of the Deep Core. This planet is reputed to be a peaceful and beautiful world. Orbiting a binary system of a blue star and blue dwarf companion, Byss is bathed in soothing blue-green sunlight, which fluoresces the microscopic life in lake and river chains dotting the surface. Mild seasons result from a minuscule axial tilt and a very stable geologic foundation. Storms, volcanism or other violent phenomena are extremely rare. Even the five moons have little influence on the tides.

There are no rare elements or heavy metals here, so scouts ruled out industrial use. The vegetation that grows in the mediocre soil has an almost primeval quality to it, with lichens and ferns predominating. No indigenous intelligent species evolved here and what native life there is, while largely nocturnal, is safe to observe.

Covered by wind-smoothed plateaus and canyons, this world is legendary for the calming and reputedly invigorating effect of its balmy climate. It was inevitable that the Emperor, frequently exhausted from his intense studies and the burden of rule, chose Byss as the location for his prime vacation palace. Here was a beautiful planet, safely hidden from the prying eyes of the galaxy. Natural islands and spectacular pre-Expansion Era ruins would be left intact. When the Emperor chose this world for his private reserve, no expense was spared. His personal architectural staff was granted *carte blanche* to build a citadel to Palpatine's hubris. Slaves and machinery were brought by the specially trained space pilots using encoded astrogation systems to reach Byss. It took years, but soon the planet gleamed with oddly shaped and ornate towers and complexes.

Of course, this world was not to be only for Palpatine's use. Quite the contrary: enormous leisure and habitation complexes were included in the original designs. Incredulous as the designers were, his orders were obeyed. Soon, enormous cities and resorts spread across the planet. Little could they suspect the true purpose behind this largess — Palpatine planned for millions to permanently reside here, where he and his minions could use their Dark Side skills to feed off their life energy.

Accordingly, a legend was created. A legend of a mystic siren world, whose surreal shores and glimmering oceans held the promise of contentment unattainable anywhere else. Millions applied for visas to this mysterious world,

but few ever suspected Byss lay in the Deep Core itself.

Meanwhile, Imperial Intelligence painstakingly sifted innumerable dossiers to find those most suited to the Emperor's needs. Of these, a few million per month were chosen and transported to Byss in secret. Upon arrival at Byss, they live out the rest of their lives in harmless amusements and pageants. All communications to loved ones are censored to perpetuate the myth and secrecy of this distant world.

■ Byss

Type: Dark Side-Enshrouded Terrestrial
Temperature: Temperate
Atmosphere: Type I (breathable)
Hydrosphere: Moderate
Gravity: Standard
Terrain: Urban, plateau reserves, canyons
Length of Day: 31 standard hours
Length of Year: 207 local days
Sapient Species: Humans
Starport: Imperial class
Population: 19.7 billion
Planet Function: Imperial capital
Government: Dark Side theocracy
Tech Level: Space
Major Imports: Foodstuffs, high tech, weaponry

The Imperial Citadel

Sprawling across a whole continent, the Imperial control sector is unquestionably the dark heart of Palpatine's New Order. The Imperial section is a deceptive paradise, with colorful plazas and public buildings camouflaging a massively armed and shielded defensive zone. Shipyards, fighter bases and military barracks for an entire army add to the protective enclave. Every building is dotted with the latest defense turbolasers and shock fields.

At the center of the control sector is the Emperor's Citadel, the fortress from which the new Empire is ruled. It has its own regiment of Imperial Sovereign Protectors as a house guard. Combined with the weaponry available from the defense zone, the fortress is virtually impregnable to any attack.

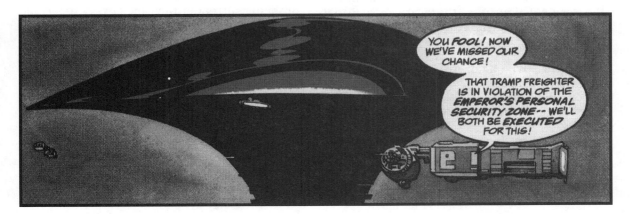

REALIZING THE EMPEROR CAN ONLY TRANSFER HIS CONSCIOUSNESS TO A LIVING BODY, LUKE LUNGES FOR THE NEAREST CLONE VAT.

ONE AFTER ANOTHER THE RUPTURED TANKS SPILL THEIR MEMBRANE-SHROUDED CONTENTS--

--ONE AFTER ANOTHER THE EMPEROR'S GENETIC OFFSPRING MEET MINDLESS BABBLING DEATH...

Looming several kilometers above the rest of the security zone, the Imperial Citadel is an ominous black spire. Inside the mazelike halls are all the facilities and computer systems necessary to command the Empire, including HoloNet communication modules, subspace transceivers and comm systems. The lower levels contain a personal audience chamber, viewing rooms and the palatial private apartments. There is a private landing bay, baths, and barracks for three legions of stormtroopers, 400 Sovereign Protectors and 600 Sentinels, and enough guest space to house dozens of Imperial Advisors in accustomed splendor. To amuse the resident courtiers, there are gladiatorial arenas, a mock combat tank, libraries, museums, internal gardens and a menagerie of exotic beasts.

For those who incur the Emperor's displeasure there is a dungeon equipped with interrogation tools terrifying beyond belief. The revived Inquisitorius is based in this section of the Citadel.

Deep inside the Citadel is the most sinister aspect of the Emperor's prototype model society. Long ago, when Palpatine first gained control over the awesome power of the Jedi Holocron, he built his Clone Labs and Dark Side sanctuary here. Training his most select servants in the ways of corruption, he made them into Dark Side Adepts, and with them, pushed the frontiers of the "science of darkness." They rediscovered forgotten and long taboo applications of the Force, chief among them the draining of life itself from the populace. What better lure for multitudes than Byss's siren call of beauty and peace? Once there, their wills are destroyed by the Emperor and his Adepts, and replaced with an illusion of tranquillity as they blissfully surrender their life energy to sustain the Emperor.

The Clone Labs

The Clone Labs are where lost science is exploited to the fullest. In it is a full library of Dark Side texts for the master's personal study. A private meditation chamber is adjacent to this library, including a small rest cubicle. Contrasting with this are his collection rooms, which are filled with ancient works of art, holo-tapestries and fine mosaics. Most precious of all is the Emperor's collection of lightsabers taken from

Jedi he has killed.

In the center of the Clone Lab complex is the Clone Vat Chamber itself. At any given time, there are at least a dozen clones in all states of growth, floating suspended in nutrient tanks, waiting for a time when the Emperor will use his powers to animate these inert forms and emerge reborn. The clones are tended night and day by the Clone Keepers and their leader, a special Dark Side Adept called the Constable of Homunculi.

The Imperial Freight Complex

As the Emperor prepared for his renewed assault on the Republic, Byss became a military staging area, refueling depot and stopover station. Traffic is still tightly controlled, but now hundreds of ships arrive on an hourly basis. As the orbiting armada gains in strength, materials and equipment of all sorts are at an all-time premium. Dozens of traders and spacers can be found in the Imperial Freight Complex located at the outskirts of the ruling city.

A three kilometer wide tower reaches from ground level to low orbit, 168 kilometers up. It is tethered to an orbital satellite, with repulsorlift generators for additional stability. The Freight Complex is where shippers, and corporate and independent ships bring military supplies and other goods to Byss. Whether it is exotic weaponry, data chips or advanced alloy hull plating, licensed Deep Core Haulers pilots can be found delivering their cargoes to the Freight Complex. Security is very tight, with Hunter-Killer probe droids and *Guardian*-class patrol ships thick as rockmites on Banthas.

To accommodate the smugglers, a complex of bistros, cabarets and leisure facilities have been built in the complex and at ground level in the spacer zones of the city. Located near the docking cradles, these businesses offer anything spacers could desire. The most popular of these is the Byss Bistro. Considered a "dive" by many corporate franchise flyers, its regular patrons swear by its atmosphere. Spacers of any species can always find something edible on the eclectic menu. Those looking for a freelance spacer are likely to find a candidate in the Bistro relaxing, negotiating deals and trading stories.

Calamari

If there was a turning point in the history of the Empire, it was when it encountered the Mon Calamari. The Mon Calamari and their Quarren neighbors had evolved on a warm and comfortable world covered by ocean, with enough reef and island area to promote technological development. They established a large, peaceful civilization. Finding space travel similar to swimming, the Mon Cals threw themselves wholeheartedly into exploration and soon mapped out all the worlds of their solar system.

When the first Calamari scout ships encountered another species, it was hoped that friendship would result. Instead of a friendly species to trade with, they ran headlong into the xenophobic and militaristic Empire. Soon an Imperial task force arrived at Calamari, intent on enslaving and exploiting the peaceful aliens. Their token resistance brushed aside, the Mon Cals and the Quarren were soon subjugated. However, unlike the hundreds of similar worlds the Empire had vanquished, the children of Calamari's seas had enough technology and spirit to begin fighting back. A species that had long despised war learned quickly from their Imperial invaders.

The Calamari sought out allies and found them in the Alliance to Restore the Republic. Uniting with the Alliance, they found their technology and industries badly needed and they put their hearts into the war effort. They learned astrogation, starship engineering and piloting and the Calamari became the backbone of the Alliance fleet. Under the leadership of Admiral Ackbar, their world was soon freed from Imperial control. More than that, Calamari became the first major system to devote its energies fully to building the Alliance's fleets. Since that time, Calamari has been defended by the Calamari Defense Forces.

Calamari's days of peace and prosperity ended when the Empire's World Devastators appeared in the skies of the world. These World Devastators proved invulnerable to nearly all the weapons at the Calamaris' disposal. As their cities were consumed and converted, the leaders drew up evacuation plans, but then R2-D2 managed to reprogram the World Devastators to turn on each other.

Now, the Mon Cal ecologists are concentrating on restoring their world to its pre-attack splendor. Of the southern territorial zone, where the Devastators launched their first assaults, the floating cities of Kee-Piru and Heurkea took the brunt of destruction. Loss of life is still being reckoned, but is expected to number in the tens of thousands at a minimum. The port city of Hikahi was partly destroyed, eliminating much of Calamari's starship building capability. The New Republic has rushed relief forces, emergency medical and food supplies and temporary shelters to house the displaced. The rebuilding efforts have begun, but it is believed that construction crews will have to spend many years

reconstructing what the Empire destroyed in just a few days.

■ Calamari

Type: Terrestrial Ocean Planet
Temperature: Temperate
Atmosphere: Type I (breathable)
Hydrosphere: Saturated
Gravity: Standard
Terrain: Ocean, reefs, floating island cities, underwater cities
Length of Day: 21 standard hours
Length of Year: 398 local days
Sapient Species: Mon Calamari (N), Quarren (N)
Starport: Imperial
Population: 11 billion Mon Calamari, 16.5 billion Quarren
Planet Function: Homeworld
Government: Representative Council
Tech Level: Space
Major Exports: High tech, warships, weaponry
Major Imports: Foodstuffs, medicine, high tech, low tech

Coruscant

Once the bright center of the galaxy, the capitol of galactic civilization lies in ruins. Home to the Republics, Old and New, and the Galactic Empire, this world has long been a beacon of progress to the civilized worlds. Once law, justice and progress had been the main concerns of those who lived on this oldest of worlds. Once there had been libraries and temples, public buildings and courts of justice. But the insanity of the Mutiny changed this.

The New Republic had spared Imperial City for precisely the reason the mutinying Imperial forces did not: as the historic center of the Old Republic, it held an enormous psychological power over the population. The Alliance had never been motivated by greed or lust for power, but by the hunger for freedom. Even the Republic, facing the new Imperial onslaught, retreated from Coruscant rather than see the capital of galactic civilization destroyed. When the Imperials began fighting among themselves, they didn't care for history or tradition. They only wanted to guarantee that what they couldn't keep wouldn't fall into enemy hands.

When the Emperor's Ruling Circle came to blows against the military, the fighting was immediate and brutal. At its worst, the equivalent of three sector battlegroups, divided among a dozen loyalties, hammered against each other in the skies above the capitol. As the navies annihilated each other, planetary bombardments were ordered, and the long siege began. Terror troops began destroying the reactors to weaken planetary shields and counter-insurgents began fighting openly in the streets and walkways of the multi-leveled cities of Coruscant.

As the shields faltered and fell, Star Destroyers began blasting cities at will. Walkers and tanks and fighters dueled non-stop for weeks. Mon Mothma and her advisors could only watch in horror as the holomedia showed Imperial weaponry set loose on a world dedicated to peace. Admiral Ackbar sent a few captured Imperial vessels to stir up trouble in other sectors to hasten the inevitable collapse in the hope that it would ultimately end the slaughter.

For those lucky enough to escape the attacks, survival is a grim prospect. Thousands of square kilometers of the planet have been transformed into burned-out wreckage. Nothing escaped the carnage: the great public transit systems, the malls, and many of the great buildings of the capitol have been gutted, bombed or smashed by walkers. Food and medical attention are almost nonexistent.

Eyewitness to Apocalypse

(The following is taken from a personal communication sent by New Republic reporter Rivoche Tarkin during the fighting on Coruscant. It was sent to Voren Na'al, Assistant Historian to the Republic.)

Voren:

It weighs on me like an unseen burden, Voren. To see this world, where I spent so much of my childhood, the capital world of the Republic, like *this* … Deities help us, the sounds at night, the fires …

It's almost more than I can bear sometimes. To think that they did this to each other. For what?

Yesterday I walked past the Temple of the Circle, or what's left of it. Now don't start again, I can hear you worrying. General Antilles insisted that I take an escort and I didn't go for a minute outside Demolinn's and Mr. Greybird's sight. We took a speeder, looking for more survivors.

It's worse than we heard. Much worse. The Mutineers are taking everything and hoarding it. They destroy what they don't want. The survivors have so little left.

General Calrissian ordered us to disperse the extra supplies to the survivors. We can't evacuate them ourselves, but later we can send some Calamari evac cruisers and save some of them. Someone has to. Even if some of them used to be COMPNOR goons, *nobody* deserves this.

It seems like the fighting has moved offworld again. For the past few days it has been like that. Scrabble around for something useful, then back up into orbit. Seems you can't look up without seeing some Imperial ship hit the atmosphere. We still hope Pinnacle Base can send someone. Calrissian claims he owes Solo some money and Solo would never let him die in that case. No one believed him, but it did raise morale some.

The ones who served here before are doing well; it's the new recruits who worry. Trouble is, I thought I overheard the commo tech, you remember Ivo, right? Well, he said he'd detected some new ships leaving hyperspace. Not Imperial. We hope they're friendly.

Give my best to Arhul and tell him to keep off the leg. Not everyone in History Section gets an assassination attempt. Much less survives it.

Hope this gets to you …

Since so much of Coruscant is covered by city, there is not enough arable land to feed the population without constant imports. The military siege has effectively blockaded the planet. The death toll is unknown, but probably ranks second only to the destruction of Alderaan. Many have gone into hiding in the mountains waiting for rescue. Instead of relief however, the anarchy has called the opportunistic. Scavengers and looters have braved the dying conflict to gut and pillage a thousand generations of culture and history.

Bleak as the situation seems, there is room for optimism. A planet is a hardy thing, and the destruction has mainly been immediately around Imperial City. With the defeat of the Emperor, it is believed that the fighting will end soon as the Imperial forces shore up their holdings. Given time, the world can be rebuilt and restored. New Republic planners have high hopes to remake the capitol and rededicate it to the ideals of civilization.

■ Coruscant

Type: Disaster world
Temperature: Temperate
Atmosphere: Type II (breath mask suggested); with terraforming, the atmosphere could return to Type I (breathable)
Hydrosphere: Moderate
Gravity: Standard
Terrain: Shattered cities, craters, plains, mountains
Length of Day: 24 standard hours
Length of Year: 368 local days
Sapient Species: Humans (N)
Starport: Limited services (all other ports have been destroyed)
Population: 806 million
Planet Function: Disaster world; formerly Imperial/Republic capital
Government: Anarchy
Tech Level: Space
Major Exports: None
Major Imports: Foodstuffs, medicinal goods

Cyax System

An uncharted system distant from the fires of the Galactic Civil War, Cyax is a yellow star and it is the brightest in Varl's sky. Early in their history, the Hutts saw this star and created legends about it and its planets. As Hutts began leaving Varl, before the great war that nearly destroyed their world, they set out to explore other systems, but left Cyax alone — it was better to allow the myths to remain. Da Soocha means "Waking Planet" in Huttese and refers to myths about a vast planet-covering ocean. The ocean itself was alive and gifted with godlike intelligence.

It is unknown if they ever visited the Cyax system. They say the world is sacred, a place of legends. Certainly, it shows up on no Hutt

Ixlls

Attribute Dice: 12D
DEXTERITY 2D+1/4D
KNOWLEDGE 1D+2/3D+1
MECHANICAL 1D/2D+2
PERCEPTION 2D+2/3D+1
STRENGTH 1D/3D
TECHNICAL 1D/3D+2
Special Skills:
Dexterity skills:
Flight: This is the skill Ixlls use to fly.
Special Abilities:
Flight: Ixlls are capable of true flight in their home planet's low gravity at a Move of 28 (about 80 KMH). In regular gravity, they can glide without difficulty at a Move of 14 (about 40 KMH).
Sonar: Ixlls have normal vision augmented by sonar, allowing them to fly safely at night, or when the sun is eclipsed by Da Soocha (a frequent occurrence). They suffer no penalty for movement in dark.
Droid Programming: Ixlls have very high pitched voices to communicate over long distances in the thin air at the top of their perches. Their language consists of chirps, clicks and whistles.
The Ixlls learned how to use their voices to communicate with R2 units and other droids that use such information-dense languages (this counts as a different language).
Story Factors:
Friendliness: Ixlls are quite playful and think of the New Republic officers and troops as new and interesting people to play with. They are quite pleased to have so many guests at one time and especially like the New Republic droids.
Pranks: There has been some minor trouble with playful Ixlls "accidentally" reprogramming the astromech droids. Sometimes this amounts to little more than a droid screwing up a repair job. In other cases, some Ixlls have lured the droids away to give as gifts to one another. The Ixlls find this quite amusing; the Republic diplomats are trying to politely resolve the matter.
Move: 6/8 (walking), 28/34 (flying; figure half the flying value for gliding speeds on standard gravity worlds)
Size: 1.4 meters long, 4 meter wingspan

Capsule: Evolved from omnivorous predators, Ixlls have a well developed society, and are clever toolmakers. Though xenologists are still studying their nuances, they are very friendly to the Republic personnel and in many cases have "adopted" certain people. Ixll society is feudal in structure, but is generally peaceful. They make simple, but elegant crafts such as leather bags and ornaments.

They are very curious about nature and life beyond the home planet. They have developed the scientific method and are quickly learning about technologies such as robotics, computers, repulsorlift and starship engines. They are developing their chemical sciences. They use several unique defenses against enemies. The most advanced of these are so-called "exploding stones" (black powder grenades) kept in pouches around their necks.

Ixlls live in warrens built at the flattened tops of the columns. They like collecting odds and ends to decorate these nests. Often, stolen Rebel equipment is a part of the collection.

astrogation charts, with a notable exception. Jabba himself had the coordinates in his databases. Some think he planned to build a new floating palace there. After his demise, Da Soocha would have remained an obscure myth were it not for a plucky astromech droid named R2-D2 who infiltrated Jabba's computers.

Once at Sullust, the droid gave the system coordinates to the Rebellion's officers and eventually Rebel scouts investigated. Interestingly, one planet is indeed covered by a vast ocean, however they found no sign of intelligent life. Of course, the surveys were admittedly brief. The Alliance named the world Da Soocha, after the legend.

When the Republic relocated, they chose the fifth moon of this world, the Pinnacle Moon, to serve as their command base. With the recent attacks on the Mon Calamari homeworld, Admiral Ackbar chose the main world of Da Soocha itself as a potential refuge for his people. Since only the most cursory examinations beneath the surface of this world have been made, it is still a mystery what life exists there. With the current conflict, further explorations of Da Soocha can wait.

Pinnacle Base (Da Soocha V)

As New Republic strategists on Coruscant observed the battles in the nearby Kaikielius and Metellos systems, many were already convinced that Imperial City would again live up to its name. It was imperative to select a new command base immediately. The base had to be secret so that the Rebellion could hide its military leaders from Imperial assassins, yet had to be near enough to trade routes to allow the Republic to effectively govern the territory that remained.

With time running out, the options narrowed. Eventually, the Pinnacle Moon was selected as the most suitable location, especially because its location had never been registered on the Haven list, which had fallen into Imperial hands.

The moon that greeted their transports was certainly unusual. Pinnacle is an old world, geologically speaking. Billions of years ago, as the surface was first forming, powerful volcanic eruptions spewed superheated minerals high into the air. The effect of Da Soocha's heavy gravity with this world's light gravity created immense tidal forces, which washed away the sedimentary layers of soil, leaving the pinnacles.

Many kilometers high, these pillars were hollowed out by erosion. Many forms of plant and animal life live inside these columns, creating the illusion of a sparse, desolate world. One effect of Da Soocha V's unique environment is

that nearly all higher forms can fly. The most highly evolved are the Ixlls, small, intelligent mammals inhabiting upper strata of the columns. With fusion drills, technicians cut into the few lifeless columns, and built facilities there.

With the final assault of the Empire, Pinnacle Base's location is no longer a secret and the Rebel Alliance is now trying to find an appropriate location for a new command base.

■ Pinnacle Moon of Da Soocha

Type: Terrestrial Satellite
Temperature: Temperate
Atmosphere: Type I (breathable)
Hydrosphere: Moist
Gravity: Light
Terrain: Mesas, pinnacle spires, mountains, oceans
Length of Day: 22 standard hours
Length of Year: 371 local days
Sapient Species: Humans, Ixlls (N)
Starport: Imperial class
Population: 321,000 Humans, 1.5 million Ixlls
Planet Function: Homeworld, New Republic command base
Government: New Republic
Tech Level: Space
Major Exports: Military supplies, high technology, troops
Major Imports: Medicine, low tech, mid tech, foodstuffs

■ Tumnor

Type: Vicious Winged Predator
DEXTERITY 3D+2
PERCEPTION 4D
Search 5D+1
STRENGTH 4D
Special Abilities:
Teeth: Do STR+2D damage
Claws: Do STR+1D damage
Move: 10 (walking), 25 (flying)
Size: 5-meter wingspan

Capsule: The Ixlls main natural enemy seems to be the tumnor. Tumnors are large winged predators. Apparently they are especially fond of Ixll young. They occupy a large role in the Ixlls' legends and myths, always taking the role of a dangerous and mercilessly evil species, ready to swoop down on defenseless Ixlls. No tumnor has been observed yet by Republic scientists.

Nal Hutta System

The Hutts claim to have evolved on the world of Varl. According to legend, once their world was a rich, lush forest world with two suns. The Hutts believe that one of the two suns crashed into a black hole and the explosion seared Varl's surface, while meteor showers rained down, leaving it a blasted, desert planet. Most of the indigenous life became extinct, but the Hutts survived and prevailed. This is the source of their greatest pride. Despite obvious scientific flaws in this myth, there is no disputing that Varl is a barren harsh world today.

Like other species, Hutts spread to many other worlds. As they fled Varl, they claimed Nal Hutta as a new homeworld. As they came to be major players in the galactic underworld, they have earned enough wealth to buy their own sectors of space.

One system that attracted initial interest from the Hutts was the Y'Toub system, where a pleasant yellow star shone over six planets, four habitable. The largest, Evocar, despite its huge size, had an extremely low density. With almost no heavy metals, the gravity is comparable to a standard world. Home to a species of humanoids called the Evocii, their civilization was in a primitive, feudal state of development.

Upon discovering them, the Hutts offered to sell the Evocii modern technology. The Hutts traded the technology for real estate — the Evocii never suspected the Hutts were trying to buy the planet away from them. By the time they learned what the Hutts were up to, construction teams had begun arriving. Soon, they replaced Evocii lodges with fantastic palaces and pleasure pavilions, which dot the surface to this day. The Evocii appealed to the Republic, but even a Jedi can't find a loophole in a Hutt contract. The Evocii were relocated to a nearby moon.

Now in secure control of Evocar, the final transformation began. The last native structures were torn down to make room for theme parks and palaces. The ancient monuments were replaced with Hutt shrines and the planet was renamed Nal Hutta, which means "Glorious Jewel" in Huttese. Whether this refers to the planet's climate or its population is unknown, but in any case, it is an apt description of this pleasant and beautiful world. Regardless, Nal Hutta's nearness to then current hyperspace routes soon made it one of the galaxy's most popular trade worlds. For a price, albeit a stiff one, anything could be bought.

This was one of the first planets bought by Hutts and it has become synonymous with Hutt crime clans. The late Jabba himself was born here on the private estates of his family. The planet is ruled by a council of the elders of each clan who live here. This world is home to a full-fledged Hutt society.

Though the planet is owned by Hutts and according to tradition Huttese is the only language permitted to be spoken here, there are many non-Hutt residents as part of the enormous class of slaves, servants and sycophants to be found anywhere Hutts reside.

From here they control the entire economic life of the moon, Nar Shaddaa, an ancient spacer's base and home to many of the pilots and techs working for the Hutt smuggling guilds. Those earning the Hutt's gratitude are often brought here for audience and vacation. Those who earn

AS HAN THREADS THE FALCON INTO THE MILES-HIGH GRID OF DECAYING PORT CITIES AND DOCKING TOWERS, CHEWBACCA EXCHANGES CONCUSSION FIRE WITH THEIR PURSUERS--

GOOD SHOOTIN', CHEWIE! *THAT'LL* TEACH THOSE SPACE PUNKS!

their wrath can sometimes be found orbiting in-between both planets.

■ Nal Hutta

Type: Large terrestrial
Temperature: Temperate
Atmosphere: Type I (breathable)
Hydrosphere: Moist
Gravity: Standard
Terrain: Urban, mountainous rain forests
Length of Day: 87 standard hours
Length of Year: 413 local days
Sapient Species: Humans, Hutts, various aliens
Starport: 1 Imperial class
Population: 3 billion Hutts, 4 billion of other species
Planet Function: Homeworld, trade, crime
Government: Clan council
Tech Level: Space
Major Exports: Tourism, contraband goods
Major Imports: Foodstuffs, high technology, luxury goods

Nar Shaddaa

The largest of Nal Hutta's moons, Nar Shaddaa, was deeded over to the Evocii as a new home-land. It was said that Nar Shaddaa had a much less favorable climate for Hutts, so they would allow the Evocii to live in peace. Unknown to the Evocii, Hutt "business" leaders bribed the nego-tiators so the Evocii could remain in-system as cheap labor. The Evocii tried to maintain their traditional lifestyle, but as Nal Hutta saw more and more trade, the Hutts confiscated more and more land (of course, the Hutts had hidden loopholes in the contract, so this action was perfectly legal). As the Hutts bought more and more of the burgeoning industries, the Evocii eventually became more and more exploited until they became a degenerate sub-class in the lowest hidden tunnels and sectors of the world covering city.

Once, the system was an important way sta-tion in galactic shipping. The structures for such trading remain today. Nar Shaddaa's refu-eling spires reach to orbit, and repair and load-ing docks sprout from the surface. As the centu-ries passed, layer after layer of city was built on top of previous levels until the surface was entirely covered in a multi-story vertical city. Lower levels fell into decay and those who couldn't afford to relocate higher were marginalized and forgotten. Among these unfor-tunates are the mutated descendants of the Evocii.

Of course, galactic tastes change, and so Nar Shaddaa fell out of favor. Once Nar Shaddaa was a bustling world of industry and trade. Luxury liners, bulk freighters and oreships pulled in here regularly to dock at the spires of port facilities and hotel complexes, but that was a long time ago. The realignment of trade routes dealt the last blow, siphoning off the last legiti-mate investors, and so criminals, slavers, droid-nappers and spice-jackers rule openly. Nar Shaddaa's glory days passed from the history tapes.

Today, Nar Shaddaa is far from the major hyperspace lanes and trade routes, a victim of the evolving economy of the galaxy. But that suits its inhabitants just fine — they prefer as little attention from the authorities as possible. Without shame or scruples, the criminal groups owned or tolerated by the Hutts rule unchal-lenged. For a price, anything in the galaxy can be bought and sold. Once a glittering gem to the wealthy, Nar Shaddaa is a tarnished and gloomy refuge for the dregs of the universe.

Of all the concerns here, none is as important as the smuggling trade. Nar Shaddaa is often called the "Smuggler's Moon." Making use of the distance from galactic commercial centers, rings of smugglers and the infamous smuggling guilds own and maintain networks of cargo transfer points and shipping routes that appear on no

Imperial charts. Here, any number of intermediaries can fence anything from spice to stolen ships on the Invisible Market. Every hour, thousands of exotic ships buzz the skies, heading to one docking sector or another. Each sector is its own bustling city where pilots, bounty hunters or pirates can cut deals of any kind.

■ Nar Shaddaa

Type: Terrestrial
Temperature: Temperate
Atmosphere: Type I (breathable)
Hydrosphere: Moist
Gravity: Standard
Terrain: Urban
Length of Day: 87 standard hours
Length of Year: 413 local days
Sapient Species: Evocii, Humans, Hutts, many other aliens
Starport: Stellar
Population: 72.1 to 94.7 billion (estimated)
Planet Function: Trade
Government: Organized crime
Tech Level: Space (upper levels), varies by sectors and part of the planet
Major Exports: Contraband, mid tech, high tech, weapons, spice, slaves
Major Imports: Contraband, mid tech, high tech, weapons, spice, slaves

The Corellian Sector

Whole smuggling communities have relocated to Nar Shaddaa. This is because the Empire secretly tolerates them here. As long as Hutts know their place and keep to it, the Empire is content to leave them and their employees unmolested. After all, they can occasionally prove useful by providing bounty hunter muscle or information.

Perhaps the most famous of these émigré communities are the Corellians. As a wise person once said, not all Corellians are smugglers, but the best smugglers are Corellians. The smuggling guilds migrated to Nar Shaddaa to avoid "Imperial entanglements" and the Empire preferred criminals to Rebels.

Unlike most smuggling guilds here, the Corellians are not controlled by the Hutts, since Corellians are fiercely self-reliant. However, the times of the independent operator are fast disappearing and every year brings them perilously close to being forced to sell out to the Hutts. Still, Corellian luck may just hold out until better times come and the guilds can get out from under the shadow of Nal Hutta.

Chapter Six
Starships

Overview

New Ships for a New Conflict

Starships have been engaging in combat nearly as long as they have existed. From the earliest atomic rockets with primitive laser armaments, to Expansion Era cruisers such as the *Gilagimar*, to the Republic's battle vessels, to the amazing Super Star Destroyers of the Empire, ships have traded fire in the depths of space.

Unfortunately, nothing inspires scientific development as much as warfare. Just as energy shields were first developed to counter the increasing damage blasters and turbolasers inflicted on ships' hulls, so too have modern developments begun a spiral of development and counter-development.

Emperor Palpatine was responsible for driving military investment and development over the past few decades, resulting in many new scientific advances. With his newly reorganized and centralized navy and army, there was nothing to stop the self-proclaimed Emperor from seizing total control. However, he didn't count on the resourcefulness of those who opposed him.

In an escalating arms race for supremacy, the Empire has spent quintillions of credits on new weapons systems, from gravity well projectors to cloaking devices, all in an attempt to stem the tide of revolt. While the Rebels have countered this with skill and daring, scientific research gained an increasing share of Alliance funding as the war dragged on.

In recent times, the Imperial Civil War has overshadowed the Galactic Civil War. The past year has seen the development of many new technologies for the battlefield — starfighters have been further miniaturized while packing more offensive punch, fully mechanized droid combat vehicles are beginning to become practical, and improved manufacturing processes have allowed the Empire and the Republic to begin the construction of fleets at an unprecedented rate.

The Eclipse

As long as there have been space fleets, there have been ships designed as command ships, specially armed and armored to serve as symbols of a civilization's power and prestige. Commanded by warlords or generals, they have often turned the tide of battles. The *Eclipse,* first in a line of new Super Star Destroyers, was the Emperor's flagship at the Battle of Pinnacle Base; unfortunately for the Empire, the *Eclipse* was destroyed in that fateful confrontation.

The history of the *Eclipse*-class Super Star Destroyers is worth noting. This ship was commissioned by Palpatine, to be designed to fit his exact specifications. It was to be the latest in a long line of super weapons. Years in the making, the first of these, the *Eclipse,* was first planned following the Battle of Hoth. After the Battle of Endor, many suggested the ship be scrapped in favor of more Star Destroyers, yet construction always continued.

When finally launched, six years after Endor, the prototype, with its ebony alloyed hull, incorporated all the significant weapons improvements of the past few decades, including gravity well projectors, improved ion cannons and new enhanced hyperdrive and sublight engines for maximum reaction speed. Fifty TIE Interceptor and eight TIE bomber squadrons nestled inside cavernous hangars large enough for an entire *Victory*-class Star Destroyer. Measuring over 17,000 meters long, the *Eclipse* was one of the largest fighting ships ever constructed.

All troops on board are specially selected, including a newly formed legion of Royal Guards and a COMPForce Assault Battalion. There are support troops to man the five prefabricated garrison bases and 100 multi-environment All Terrain Armored Transports. The Emperor has also added a cadre of Sovereign Protectors as his personal bodyguards.

The most important advancement in the *Eclipse* is its main weapon: a spine-mounted

THE EMPEROR'S COMMAND VESSEL, TEN MILES FROM STEM TO STERN, SEEMS DESIGNED TO INSPIRE *DREAD* IN EVERY POSSIBLE OPPONENT.

BUT LEIA'S FRIENDS IN THE ALLIANCE UNDERSTAND THAT WHAT IS ABOUT TO HAPPEN TRANSCENDS THE TECHNOLOGY OF WAR...

THE CONFRONTATION WITH THE EMPEROR--AND THE FATE OF THE GALAXY--IS A MATTER ONLY A *JEDI* CAN RESOLVE.

superlaser modeled on the main weapon of the Death Star itself. The Death Star's prime weapon was composed of eight individual lasers that could focus together, generating enough power to destroy an entire planet. By comparison, the *Eclipse* carries only a single laser, but recent focussing and generator advances make this ray much more powerful than the units used on the Death Star. The beam packs enough destructive power to shatter the most powerful planetary shields and sear whole continents in a flash.

■ The Eclipse

Craft: KDY's *Eclipse*-class Super Star Destroyer
Type: Super Star Destroyer
Scale: Capital
Length: 17,500 meters
Skill: Capital ship piloting: Super Star Destroyer
Crew: 708,470, gunners: 4,175, skeleton: 88,500/+10
Crew Skill: Astrogation 5D, capital ship gunnery 5D, capital ship piloting 6D, capital ship shields 4D+2, sensors 4D+1
Passengers: 150,000 (troops)
Cargo Capacity: 600,000 metric tons
Consumables: 10 years
Cost: Not available for sale
Hyperdrive Multiplier: x2
Hyperdrive Backup: x6
Nav Computer: Yes
Maneuverability: 1D
Space: 4
Hull: 15D+2
Shields: 11D+1
Sensors:
  Passive: 250/2D
  Scan: 350/3D
  Search: 500/4D
  Focus: 75/5D

Weapons:
  Axial Superlaser
    Fire Arc: Front
    Crew: 75
    Scale: Death Star
    Skill: Capital ship gunnery: superlaser
    Fire Control: 5D
    Space Range: 5-25/75/150
    Damage: Gradational output can fire once every minute at minimum energy (1D damage). It can also build a charge of 1D per minute up to 8D. Current reactor can only generate 11D total per day.
  550 Heavy Laser Cannons
    Fire Arc: 200 front, 150 left, 150 right, 50 back
    Crew: 4
    Skill: Capital ship gunnery
    Fire Control: 2D
    Space Range: 3-15/35/75
    Atmosphere Range: 6-15/72/150KM
    Damage: 8D
  500 Turbolaser Batteries
    Fire Arc: 150 front, 125 left, 125 right, 100 back
    Crew: 2
    Scale: Starfighter
    Skill: Starship Gunnery
    Fire Control: 4D
    Space Range: 3-15/36/75
    Atmosphere Range: 600-1.5/7/15KM
    Damage: 5D
  75 Ion Cannon
    Fire Arc: 25 front, 25 left, 25 right
    Crew: 4
    Skill: Capital ship gunnery
    Fire Control: 2D+2
    Space Range: 1-10/25/50
    Atmosphere Range: 2-20/50/100KM
    Damage: 3D
  100 Tractor Beam Emplacements
    Fire Arc: 55 front, 20 left, 20 right, 5 back
    Crew: 5
    Skill: Capital ship gunnery

Fire Control: 4D
Space Range: 1-5/15/30
Atmosphere Range: 2-10/30/60 KM
Damage: 6D

10 Gravity Well Projectors
Fire Arc: 3 front, 2 left, 2 right, 3 back
Crew: 10
Skill: Capital ship gunnery: gravity well projector
Fire Control: 4D
Space Range: 1-5/15/30
Damage: Blocks hyperspace travel*

*See pages 18–20 of *Wanted by Cracken* for complete rules.

The Sovereign

A less powerful design of the *Eclipse*-class has been created named the *Sovereign*-class (it still overwhelms the original Super Star Destroyer design). The Emperor envisioned a fleet of these vessels. The first of the line, still under construction, is the *Sovereign*. Other potential ships in the line include the *Autarch*, *Despot* and *Heresiarch*.

Unlike the *Eclipse,* the *Sovereign*-class only carries 35 squadrons of TIE Interceptors and five of Bombers. It carries only 75 All Terrain Armored vehicles.

■ The Sovereign

Craft: KDY's *Sovereign*-class Super Star Destroyer
Type: Super Star Destroyer
Scale: Capital
Length: 15,000 meters
Skill: Capital ship piloting
Crew: 601,670, gunners: 4,075, skeleton: 86,000/+10
Crew Skill: Astrogation 4D+1, capital ship gunnery 4D+1, capital ship piloting 4D, capital ship shields 4D, sensors 3D+1
Passengers: 130,100 (troops)
Cargo Capacity: 400,000 metric tons
Consumables: 5 years
Cost: Not available for sale
Hyperdrive Multiplier: x3
Hyperdrive Backup: x8
Nav Computer: Yes
Maneuverability: 1D
Space: 3
Hull: 11D
Shields: 8D
Sensors:
Passive: 250/2D
Scan: 350/3D
Search: 500/4D
Focus: 70/5D
Weapons:
Axial Superlaser
Fire Arc: Front
Crew: 75
Scale: Death Star
Skill: Capital ship gunnery: superlaser
Fire Control: 5D
Space Range: 5-25/75/150
Damage: Gradational Output can fire once every minute at minimum energy (1D damage). It can also build a charge of 1D per minute up to 8D. Current reactor can only generate 8D total per day.
500 Heavy Laser Cannons
Fire Arc: 200 front, 150 left, 150 right

Crew: 4
Skill: Capital ship gunnery
Fire Control: 2D
Space Range: 3-15/35/75
Atmosphere Range: 6-15/72/150KM
Damage: 8D

500 Turbolaser Batteries
Fire Arc: 150 front, 125 left, 125 right, 100 back
Crew: 2
Scale: Starfighter
Skill: Starship Gunnery
Fire Control: 4D
Space Range: 3-15/36/75
Atmosphere Range: 600-1.5/7/15KM
Damage: 5D

75 Ion Cannon
Fire Arc: 25 front, 25 left, 25 right
Crew: 6
Skill: Capital ship gunnery
Fire Control: 2D+2
Space Range: 1-10/25/50
Atmosphere Range: 2-20/50/100KM
Damage: 3D

100 Tractor Beam Emplacements
Fire Arc: 55 front, 20 left, 20 right, 5 back
Crew: 5
Skill: Capital ship gunnery
Fire Control: 4D
Space Range: 1-5/15/30
Atmosphere Range: 2-10/30/60 KM
Damage: 6D

5 Gravity Well Projectors
Fire Arc: 3 front, 1 left, 1 right
Crew: 10
Skill: Capital ship gunnery: gravity well projector
Fire Control: 4D
Space Range: 1-/15/30
Damage: Blocks Hyperspace Travel*

*See pages 18–20 of *Wanted by Cracken* for complete rules.

The Defiance

When the Mon Calamari first joined the Rebel Alliance, they realized their greatest contribution would be to the navy. Their latest effort is the MC90 cruiser, the first line of Mon Cal cruisers expressly designed for combat. The MC90 has many improvements over the original MC80 design.

First, the ship line is more modularized. While each individual ship is still a work of art, the internal components and systems are more consistently arranged to aid non-Mon Cal techs who must work on the ship. Second, all the controls and displays have multiple wavelength settings so that crewmembers of any species can crew the ships (the original MC80s had displays designed specifically for the Mon Cals' viewing wavelength, meaning the Human and other alien crewmembers couldn't read vital information). The 90s have increased drive, maneuverability and shielding systems, as well as many more weapons. Naturally, the ship has an upgraded power generator system to handle the increased power demand. Finally, the ships have more interior cargo space, allowing them to carry a full 72 starfighters (two wings), making the MC90s the equivalent of a Star Destroyer in terms of fighter compliment. The first of the MC90 line is the *Defiance,* which now serves as Admiral Ackbar's flagship.

■ The Defiance

Craft: Mon Calamari MC90 Star Cruiser
Type: Star Cruiser
Scale: Capital
Length: 1,255 meters
Skill: Capital ship piloting: Mon Cal cruiser
Crew: 5,860, gunners: 605, skeleton: 1,350/+10
Crew Skill: Astrogation 4D, capital ship gunnery 5D, capital ship piloting 6D, capital ship shields 5D+1, sensors 4D
Passengers: 1,700 (troops)
Cargo Capacity: 30,000 metric tons
Consumables: 2 years
Cost: Not available for sale
Hyperdrive Multiplier: x1
Hyperdrive Backup: x9
Nav Computer: Yes
Maneuverability: 3D
Space: 7
Hull: 7D
Shields: 6D*
* The MC90 has 6D of back-up shields. When a die of shields is lost, if the shield operators can make an Easy *capital ship shields* total, one of the back-up die codes of shields can be added to the reduced shield code up to its original 6D value.
Sensors:
 Passive: 40/1D
 Scan: 60/2D
 Search: 120/3D
 Focus: 5/4D
Weapons:
 75 Turbolaser Batteries
 Fire Arc: 30 front, 15 left, 15 right, 15 back
 Crew: 3
 Skill: Capital ship gunnery
 Fire Control: 2D

 Space Range: 3-15/35/75
 Atmosphere Range: 6-30/70/150KM
 Damage: 4D
 30 Ion Cannon Batteries
 Fire Arc: 10 front, 8 left, 8 right, 4 back
 Crew: 7
 Skill: Capital ship gunnery
 Fire Control: 3D
 Space Range: 1-10/25/50
 Atmosphere Range: 2-20/50/100KM
 Damage: 3D
 8 Tractor Beam Projectors
 Fire Arc: 5 front, 1 left, 1 right, 1 back
 Crew: 10
 Skill: Capital ship gunnery
 Fire Control: 2D+2
 Space Range: 1-5/15/30
 Atmosphere Range: 2-10/30/60KM
 Damage: 4D
 6 Proton Torpedo/Missile Tubes
 Fire Arc: 6 front
 Crew: 15
 Skill: Capital ship gunnery
 Fire Control: 3D+2
 Space Range: 2-12/30/60
 Atmosphere Range: 200-1.2/3/6KM
 Damage: 6D+1

Imperial Dungeon Ships

Imperial dungeon ships were introduced at the height of the Purge in an attempt to control Jedi Knights and other dangerous prisoners. Originally designed by the Mandalorians, the majority of the ship's cells were devoted to common prisoners. Sections were partitioned off to allow for variable gravity, lighting, atmosphere and other factors — often prisoners were held under uncomfortable conditions (such as heavier than normal gravity) to keep them docile during the prisoner transfer. Other tactics of control included mild electric shocks

ADMIRAL ACKBAR, ABOARD THE CALAMARI FLAGSHIP *DEFIANCE,* HAS JUST RETURNED FROM A RECONNAISSANCE MISSION TO THE INNERMOST QUADRANT OF THE GALAXY...

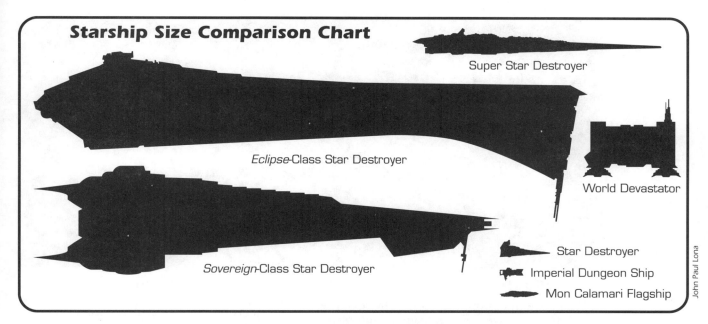

Starship Size Comparison Chart

Super Star Destroyer

Eclipse-Class Star Destroyer

World Devastator

Sovereign-Class Star Destroyer

Star Destroyer

Imperial Dungeon Ship

Mon Calamari Flagship

John Paul Lona

(painful but causing no permanent damage), sirens and hallucinogenic gases. Prisoners were guarded by droids along with normal organic guards (who were heavily armed and ordered to maintain order no matter what happened). Since the prisoners knew that disobedience meant death, there were few uprisings aboard the dungeon ships.

When it came to Jedi Knights, the prison ships were designed on the principle that the best way to keep a Jedi Knight under control was to keep him disoriented and preoccupied with survival. Traditional restraints were useless against those who could call upon the Force. Super-dense alloys lined each cell to prevent any physical escape and, it was (erroneously) hoped, to screen out any telepathy. Eventually, the energy shields used on the Universal Energy Cages had to be installed around the perimeter of the cells to prevent the Jedi from using their abilities. Life support settings were set extremely low to force the Jedi into hibernating for the duration of the voyage.

To prevent prisoners from commandeering vessels, the dungeon ships lack a normal nav computer. The computer can only hold two sets of coordinates at any given time: the jump to the prisoner transfer planet and the final destination. If a dungeon ship had to make multiple jumps, it would have to get new jump coordinates at each stopover. The bridge is located at the bottom of the ship in a self contained and detachable command chamber equipped with emergency rations and a signal beacon.

■ Imperial Dungeon Ships

Craft: Rendili StarDrive's *Lictor*-class
Type: Mandalorian Dungeon Ship
Scale: Capital
Length: 764 meters
Skill: Capital ship piloting: *Lictor*-class
Crew: 860, gunners: 46, skeleton: 370/+15
Crew Skill: Astrogation 2D, capital ship gunnery 4D+1, capital ship piloting 4D, capital ship shields 4D, sensors 3D
Passengers: 400 (security wardens), 8,000 (prisoners in standard cells), 1,000 (prisoners in special holding cells)
Cargo Capacity: 1,500 metric tons
Consumables: 2 months
Cost: 7.8 million credits
Hyperdrive Multiplier: x2
Nav Computer: Limited to two jumps
Maneuverability: 3D
Space: 3
Hull: 5D
Shields: 1D+2
Sensors:
  Passive: 40/OD
  Scan: 75/1D
  Search: 150/3D
  Focus: 4/4D+2
Weapons:
  10 Quad Turbolaser Batteries
    Fire Arc: 2 front, 4 left, 4 right
    Crew: 3
    Skill: Capital ship gunnery
    Fire Control: 2D
    Space Range: 3-15/35/75
    Atmosphere Range: 6-30/70/150KM
    Damage: 4D
  2 Tractor Beam Projectors
    Fire Arc: 1 front/left, 1rear/right*
    * May be used on only one fire arc per round.
    Crew: 8
    Skill: Capital ship gunnery
    Fire Control: 2D
    Space Range: 1-15/15/35
    Atmosphere Range: 2-10/30/60KM
    Damage: 4D

Taskforce Cruiser

When one thinks of the Imperial starfleet, the great Star Destroyers, Dreadnaughts and other warships of the line come easily to mind. Important as they are, no less needed are the uncounted support vessels that maintain Imperial presence and perform the less glorious tasks of the Navy. Chief among these are the hospital cruisers, communications ships and survey cruisers.

Previously, the Empire maintained thousands of each different type of craft. The sector and oversector Navy worlds had to carry dozens of support ships to cover any contingency. Colony exploration might require survey or first contact ships. Mop-up after battles required both salvage and hospital ships. Spy cruisers were always useful for monitoring pirates and potential Rebel activity. Many ships weren't in common use, but it was better to have too many ships than not enough. Still, it took money from warship production.

Following a report on streamlining fleet operations, a new approach was urged and from proposals, Tagge Industries won the contract and construction began in earnest. The result was the modular taskforce cruiser. Realizing the underlying design for many of these craft is very similar, rather than make the same ship over for new functions, the design was a ship that could be reconfigured as needed. The cruiser boasts a single framework, including engines, skeleton crew quarters, life support system and command compartments. Interchangeable modules with mission specific equipment can be added as necessary. With only a day at a space station or orbital facility, a hospital cruiser can be transformed into a long range scout or mining survey explorer.

The cruiser's weaponry is quite light for a ship of this size, but the cruiser's main mission is not combat, but support. In dangerous situations, a group of these cruisers will often have an armed escort.

■ Modular Taskforce Cruiser

Craft: Tagge Industries Shipyards Ltd. Modular Taskforce Cruiser
Type: Multi-task medium transport
Scale: Capital
Length: 1,150 meters
Skill: Capital ship piloting: taskforce cruiser
Crew: Varies according to mission profile
Passengers: Varies according to mission profile
Cargo Capacity: Varies according to mission profile
Consumables: 6 months
Cost: 2.5 million (base cruiser), additional cost for individual modules
Hyperdrive Multiplier: x3
Hyperdrive Backup: x7
Nav Computer: Yes
Maneuverability: 2D
Space: 4
Atmosphere: 280; 800KMH
Hull: 3D+1
Shields: 2D
Sensors:
    Standard sensor suite; more advanced sensors can be installed as needed
    Passive: 40/1D
    Scan: 60/2D
    Search: 120/3D
    Focus: 5/4D
Weapons:
    15 Medium Turbolasers
      Fire Arc: 10 forward, 5 back
      Crew: 2
      Skill: Capital ship gunnery
      Fire Control: 3D
      Space Range: 3-15/35/75
      Atmosphere Range: 6-30/70/150KM
      Damage: 5D

Mission Function Modules

Each individual mission function module is an entirely self-contained unit. The module need only be attached to the skeleton and be hooked into the power generators, life support and communications ports.

Each ship can only contain one module at a time. It is believed that Tagge Industries is working on mini-modules so a ship can be outfitted for a variety of smaller-scale functions.

Typical Mission Function Modules (MFMs) are as follows:

■ Hospital Module

Crew: 225 doctors, 400 nurses, 1,500 emergency medical technicians, 1,000 medical droids
Passengers: 2,750 (bacta tanks), 1,000 (quarantine ward), 19,600 (patients)
Cargo Capacity: 5,000 metric tons
Cost: 750,000 credits

Capsule: The hospital module is used in planetary disasters, anti-terrorist clean-up functions and space battle recovery. The hospital module can handle any number of disasters from combat, to radiation leaks. Equipment includes thousands of medpacs, repulsorlift stretchers, five shuttles for transporting casualties and a centralized medical computer.

■ Survey Module

Crew: 2,000 scouts, 1,500 techs, 5,000 droids
Cost: 1 million credits
Sensors:
Passive: 60/3D
Scan: 80/4D
Search: 175/5D
Focus: 6/5D+2

Capsule: This module is used for the rapid exploration of planets and entire systems. Besides the crew, the module contains over 100 observation airspeeders for rapid surveys, 500 exploration droids, and five Skipray blastboats and six TIE bombers for defense. The module has a centralized computer for quick analysis of all gathered data. This module and its crew can completely analyze a planet within a standard 24 hour day and determine likely colony sites, mineral and agricultural resources. The computer and its techs can also calculate likely astrogation routes from any nearby trade routes.

■ Observation Module

Crew: 1,550 Intelligence officers and comscan specialists
Cost: 6.3 million credits
Sensors:
Passive: 250/3D
Scan: 800/4D
Search: 1500/5D
Focus: 18/6D

Capsule: This module is used for espionage and long range observation for intelligence gathering. The cruiser itself does not infiltrate enemy territory since it would be easily detected by enemy sensors. Instead, the ship is equipped with 500 probots and observation droids, which are deployed around the perimeter of enemy holdings for passive observation. The probots can run the standard light/energy spectrum analysis and eavesdrop on communications frequencies. Some specially equipped (and very expensive) probots can

scan very localized hyperspace with cross-channeled radiation (as is used with the planetary security net). With the subspace link-up, the probots can be deployed up to 30 light years away and still have instantaneous communication with the cruiser. The ship has 12 TIE fighters for defense.

■ Rescue Module

Crew: 140 doctors, 2,130 techs
Cargo Capacity: 40,000 metric tons
Cost: 500,000 credits (plus parts)

Capsule: The rescue module is used for space battle clean-up and repair. When a cruiser is dispatched to a battle scene, it is loaded with a variety of replacement parts for the ships that were involved in the battle. Doctors search any wrecks that weren't already checked for survivors (presumably, a hospital ship is sent with these ships to a battle scene). The primary mission of the techs is to repair what ships they can so that they can be flown back to dockyards for complete repairs (naturally, only drive systems and life support systems are repaired at this stage). Those ships that cannot be repaired are analyzed and the techs note what must be done to the ship so that it can be returned to the nearest Imperial shipyard. Military planners at the shipyard will then determine whether repairs will be attempted or simply scuttled.

■ Inquisition Module

Crew: 100 Inquisitors, 3,660 CompForce/observation staff, 10,000 interrogation droids
Cost: 425,000 credits

Capsule: This module is the most recent addition and it is used for punitive actions against insurgents and rebellious worlds. Aboard the module's cavernous cargo holds are 15,000 pre-fabricated disintegration chambers, two garrison bases, an Orbital Data Net Eraser unit, probes with sterilization spores, five cluster bombs with magnepulse bombs (see page 67 of the *Imperial Sourcebook*) and a complete orbital nightcloak system.

The Emancipator And The Liberator

At the Battle of Endor, a huge number of Imperial ships were destroyed by the Rebel Alliance. Some ships made it to lightspeed shortly after the Emperor's death. Of the armada gathered around Endor, a few remaining ships either surrendered outright or took enough battle damage to fall into Rebel hands. Of note were the *Adjudicator* and *Accuser*, two *Imperial*-class Star Destroyers. Realizing this stroke of good luck, General Lando Calrissian suggested refitting the ships to make them spaceworthy again.

Calrissian's logic was as follows: with the battle of Endor such a panic for the Imperials, no one could know for sure how many ships got away at the end. These ships, repaired and outfitted for duty, would allow the Rebels to infiltrate the Imperial sectors without raising the kind of ruckus a Republic cruiser might. Though Admiral Ackbar found the subterfuge distasteful, he couldn't discount the potential benefits and agreed.

To give them a special advantage, some new features were to be added, including beefed-up weapons and sensors. Renamed the *Liberator* and the *Emancipator*, they were intended to play a vital role in the Borderland campaign, on the edge of Republic and Imperial space. The two Star Destroyers were holed up in the secret Hast Shipyards; however, the shipyards didn't remain a secret for long, as Imperial spies uncovered their location. The Hast Shipyards were a repair center, where damaged starships were rebuilt and refitted for combat duty. The Empire's sudden and brutal attack devastated the shipyards, nearly destroying the Star Destroyers and also damaging a large portion of the Rebel fleet — over 20 corvettes, five Nebulon-Bs and no less than seven Mon Cal MC80 cruisers were put out of commission in that battle. Casualties numbered in the thousands.

Suddenly, the repair of the Star Destroyers took a backseat to repairing the numerous other line ships that had been damaged in the battle. The Republic, always short on vessels, found itself critically short on combat ships, cutting short a planned campaign against what remained of the Empire (this single assault by the Empire helped throw the Republic's plans several *years* behind schedule).

It took a full five years for the Star Destroyers to be refitted for duty. They were nearly complete when Grand Admiral Thrawn's offensive began, further delaying the activation of the ships. Finally, after Thrawn was defeated, the ships were quietly put into service. With Lando Calrissian back in the Republic's military, he urged that the ships be put to their original use: spying on the Empire and stirring up trouble among the feuding factions.

Unfortunately, much of that work was wasted. In one of its first missions, the *Liberator* found itself caught in the heart of the Imperial Civil War and it was shot down over Coruscant. Only the skill and special abilities of Luke Skywalker prevented all hands from being killed in the crash landing.

The *Emancipator* served valiantly in the Battle of Calamari. Under the command of Calrissian and General Wedge Antilles, it destroyed the Imperial command ship *Allegiance*, buying valuable time to reinforce the frantic defenders. The Republic fleet arrived, but not in time to save *Emancipator* from being consumed by the *Silencer-7*.

■ The Emancipator and the Liberator

Craft: Kuat Drive Yards Imperial I Star Destroyer
Type: Modified Star Destroyer
Scale: Capital
Length: 1,600 meters
Skill: Capital ship piloting: Star Destroyer
Crew: 28,115, gunners: 168, skeleton: 2,300/+15
Crew Skill: Astrogation 4D+1, capital ship gunnery 5D+2, capital ship piloting 5D+2, capital ship shields 4D+1, sensors 5D
Passengers: 8,500 (troops)
Cargo Capacity: 36,000 metric tons
Consumables: 1 year
Cost: Not available for sale
Hyperdrive Multiplier: x1 1/2
Hyperdrive Backup: x8
Nav Computer: Yes
Maneuverability: 1D+2
Space: 6
Hull: 7D
Shields: 3D
Sensors:
  Passive: 60/1D
  Scan: 115/3D
  Search: 200/4D
  Focus: 7/5D
Weapons:
  60 Turbolaser Batteries
    Fire Arc: 20 front, 20 left, 20 right
    Crew: 1 (40), 2 (20)
    Skill: Capital ship gunnery
    Fire Control: 4D
    Space Range: 3-15/36/75
    Atmosphere Range: 6-15/72/150KM
    Damage: 5D
  60 Ion Cannons
    Fire Arc: 20 front, 15 left, 15 right, 10 back
    Crew: 1 (50), 2 (10)
    Skill: Capital ship gunnery
    Fire Control: 2D+2
    Space Range: 1-10/25/50
    Atmosphere Range: 2-20/30/60KM
    Damage: 3D
  6 Proton Torpedo Launchers
    Fire Arc: Front
    Crew: 3
    Skill: Capital ship gunnery
    Fire Control: 3D+2
    Space Range: 2-12/30/60
    Atmosphere Range: 200-1.2/3/6KM
    Damage: 6D+1

Mon Calamari Evacuation Carriers

The Battle of Calamari was a stern test of the fortitude and bravery of the Mon Calamari. While their floating cities were brutalized by numerous Imperial assaults, the Mon Cal engineers went to work converting the remaining cruisers, military and civilian, to evacuation ships. Techs were busy tearing out weapons systems, removing redundant shields and supplying life support to cargo holds. The techs worked at a feverish pace, converting ships to evacuation duty in just under one day per ship.

The techs were aiming for maximum occu-

pancy: as a result, the hyperdrive systems were depowered to add more life support. The evacuation cruisers could only jump a few light years to a neighboring system, where refugees were left to await final transport to a permanent colony world. In the end, each evacuation cruiser was capable of holding more than 75,000 people. Fortunately, the entire evacuation of the world proved unnecessary, but the Mon Cals proved it could be done.

■ Mon Calamari Evacuation Cruisers

Craft: Modified Mon Calamari MC80 Star Cruiser
Type: Evacuation carrier
Scale: Capital
Length: 1,200 meters
Skill: Capital ship piloting: Mon Cal cruiser
Crew: 1,011, skeleton 429/+10
Crew Skill: Astrogation 3D+2, capital ship piloting 5D, capital ship shields 5D, sensors 3D
Passengers: 75,000 (safely; this number can be doubled if absolutely necessary, but is extremely risky)
Cargo Capacity: 16,000 metric tons
Consumables: 6 weeks
Cost: Not available for sale
Hyperdrive Multiplier: x4
Hyperdrive Backup: x14
Nav Computer: Yes
Maneuverability: 0D
Space: 6
Atmosphere: 210; 600KMH
Hull: 3D
Shields: 3D
Sensors:
　　Passive: 10/1D
　　Scan: 20/2D
　　Search: 30/3D

Personal Transports and Yachts

One might get the impression that warships are the majority of space craft in existence. Nothing could be further from the truth. Combat starships may gain considerable attention, but the vast majority of space vessels are civilian craft such as freighters, traders, luxury liners and cargo transports.

Of these, the transports and freighters are among the most important. During peacetime, much of the basic cargo transport is handled by the giant corporate shipping firms, with their container ships and bulk cargo barges. However, during the constant conflict of the past few years, the huge shipping firms and bulk cargo lines refused to travel to many of the less important worlds without exorbitant insurance guarantees. Ships and freighters sat vacant on docking pads across the galaxy; even the banks couldn't foreclose without risking their investments.

The galactic economy depends on the ability to transport goods and products from one world to another, so someone must take up the slack. As the smaller worlds went neglected, goods

ran out and local economies collapsed. As the galactic economy has slowed, this vicious circle of defaulted loans, attempted foreclosures, bad credit ratings and unpaid debts have played havoc with the currency exchanges.

That is where the tramp freighter captain and the smuggler come in. This has been a boon time for the private operator, with possible fortunes just waiting to be made by the lucky, the skilled or the unscrupulous. To be sure, not all have the same attitude or background. Some are little more than criminals who will do anything for a credit, whether handling stolen goods, toxic addictives or slaves. Some are in the occasional pay of the Empire, or Hutt gangsters, or both. Still, most are at least semi-honest.

Some are heroic iconoclasts, risking their lives to bring medical supplies through Imperial blockades. Some are honest skippers driven to the occasional under-the-table deal to make payments. There are also the rogues in the spice trade, bringing luxury goods and baubles wherever the credit beckons. The New Republic has made a great effort to court them to its side and hire them to work hauling cargoes. In the past this wasn't always successful, but in light of the role Talon Karrde played to defeat the Warlord Thrawn, even Admiral Ackbar has moderated his views.

Of course, it is a seller's market in the galaxy with the civil war in full swing, and both Republic and Empire compete for the services of the best captains. While it is easy to hire a smuggler or freighter captain, it is a lot harder to buy one. Loyalty is not easily earned or given.

The Millennium Falcon

If one asked New Republic military strategists which ship is the most famous of all the ships in the New Republic armada and which has served in the widest variety of ways, most of them would have to say it has been a converted YT-1300 light freighter. The *Millennium Falcon* has been owned by two generals of the New Republic, has carried three Jedi Knights and has been instrumental in destroying two Death Stars.

Obviously this is no ordinary light freighter, and Han Solo, current owner, is no ordinary smuggler. Neither is General Lando Calrissian, the man he won it from in a sabacc game. Solo, back when he was just a smuggler (albeit one of the best around), first became familiar with the *Falcon* when Calrissian "acquired" the ship himself. Eventually, Solo managed to win the vessel and turned it into one of the fastest ships in the galaxy.

Modified extensively even before Calrissian got a hold of it, the *Falcon* has undergone modifications over the years, with upgraded shields, extra supercharged weapons systems and three different computer brains in it. Solo, his first mate Chewie, the techs at Bespin and any number of other engineers over the years have had a hand in making the *Falcon* the fine, if temperamental, ship she is today. As if that weren't enough, to keep up with an ever more dangerous galaxy, Solo had the ship recently overhauled and the latest ion engines were installed. Truly, the *Falcon* will keep at peak performance for many years to come if Solo has anything to say about it.

■ The Millennium Falcon

Craft: Corellian Engineering YT-1300
Type: Modified light freighter
Scale: Starfighter
Length: 26.7 meters
Skill: Space transports: YT-1300 transport
Crew: 2 (1 can coordinate), gunners: 2, skeleton: 1/+15
Crew Skill: See Han Solo and Chewbacca
Passengers: 6
Cargo Capacity: 100 metric tons
Consumables: 2 months
Cost: Not available for sale
Hyperdrive Multiplier: x1/2
Hyperdrive Backup: x10
Nav Computer: Yes
Maneuverability: 2D
Space: 9
Atmosphere: 415; 1,200KMH
Hull: 6D
Shields: 3D
Sensors:
    Passive: 30/1D
    Scan: 60/2D
    Search: 75/3D
    Focus: 4/4D
Weapons:
    Two Quad Laser Cannon
        Fire Arc: Turret
        Crew: 1
        Skill: Starship gunnery
        Fire Control: 3D
        Space Range: 1-3/12/25
        Atmosphere Range: 100-300/1.2/2.5KM
        Damage: 6D
    Two Concussion Missile Tubes (fire-linked)
        Fire Arc: Front
        Skill: Missile weapons: concussion missiles
        Fire Control: 3D
        Space Range: 1/3/7
        Atmosphere Range: 50-100/300/700
        Damage: 9D
    One Light Laser Cannon (retractable)
        Fire Arc: Turret
        Scale: Speeder
        Skill: Vehicle blasters
        Fire Control: 4D (fired from cockpit)
        Atmosphere Range: 1-50/100/250
        Damage: 3D

The Starlight Intruder

Every smuggler wants their ship to be the fastest, but few have the skill to do more than idly dream. Salla Zend and Shug Ninx have both worked on a number of fast ships, among them the *Millennium Falcon*, which some say is the fastest ship that ever was. If Salla and Shug have their way, the *Falcon* will one day have to settle for a close second to their own ship, the *Starlight Intruder*.

The product of years of loving work and careful customizing, the *Starlight Intruder* is the great unfinished project in Salla Zend's life. Her full time job in Shug Ninx's garage means she can only use her spare time to work on the *Intruder*. However, she only has time to work on one system at a time and by the time it is in perfect working order, some new advance or improvement catches her eye and it's back to work again.

This is not to say the *Starlight Intruder* is an unfinished or unspaceworthy vessel. Quite the contrary; it has been making very successful runs as a Deep Core Hauler for some time now. Licensed to travel beyond the Imperial Hyperspace Security Net, the *Starlight Intruder* is one of the regular freighters to carry material to Byss itself. When docked there, Salla and Shug listen for reports about new developments and refinements from other spacers. When back on Nar Shaddaa, new parts and leftover engine and drive scraps find their way to Shug's garage and into the *Intruder*.

These parts are lovingly inspected, tested, retested, installed and adjusted to the most precise tolerances. This is because Salla has always been a perfectionist. No matter how many pieces the ship may be in at any given time, when Shug gets a price on a cargo, Salla will always have the vessel spaceworthy in a matter of hours. As it is, the *Intruder* still breaks records, but always with Salla's grudging knowledge that she could have done better with more time to work on her ship. Salla has worked on many of the fastest smuggling ships in the galaxy and she is using all her considerable knowledge and talent to guarantee that someday this hotrod junkheap will be the fastest. And the best. That means potentially years more work, but to Salla it is a labor of love.

■ Starlight Intruder

Craft: Custom Mobquet Medium Cargo Hauler
Type: Modified medium transport

Scale: Starfighter
Length: 79.3 meters
Skill: Space transports: Mobquet medium transport
Crew: 2 (1 can coordinate), gunners: 2, skeleton: 1/+10
Crew Skill: See Salla Zend and Shug Ninx
Passengers: 8
Cargo Capacity: 700 metric tons
Consumables: 2 months
Cost: Not available for sale
Hyperdrive Multiplier: x3/4
Hyperdrive Backup: x11
Nav Computer: Yes
Maneuverability: 1D
Space: 6
Atmosphere: 330; 950KMH
Hull: 8D
Shields: 4D+1
Sensors:
  Passive: 30/1D
  Scan: 80/2D
  Search: 120/3D
  Focus: 4/4D
Weapons:
  Two Medium Turbolasers
    Fire Arc: Turret
    Crew: 1
    Skill: Starship gunnery
    Fire Control: 2D
    Space Range: 1-3/12/25
    Atmosphere Range: 100-300/1.2/2.5KM
    Damage: 5D

■ The Starlight Intruder

The Hyperspace Marauder

Lo Khan has owned the *Hyperspace Marauder* longer than most smugglers have been in the business. Of course, Lo Khan has been doing lots of things longer than most smugglers have been in the business. He and his partner, Luwingo, have been a team for years and both of them can be found relaxing after a long haul in cantinas and bistros from one side of the galaxy to the other. Lo Khan prefers to handle the safer Imperial runs and his ship is perfect for just that sort of duty.

The *Marauder* isn't particularly fast, but that isn't much of a problem. Neither is the lack of weaponry. Lo Khan prefers to spend his money these days on good shields and a thick hull. He keeps to well-policed routes anyway, so there isn't much need to keep the ship armed to the teeth. Let the younger crowd try outracing or shooting the pirates and other criminals out there in the void; those days are long gone for him.

Of course, there was always the chance that someone would get lucky. Once they got inside the ship things would get interesting. Then they had to deal with Luwingo. If they went for a weapon, Luwingo might get angry. If they tried to tow the ship or cut into the bay, Luwingo would have time to patch into their onboard computer systems and shut their ship down. Either way, it ends pretty much the same: him and Luwingo making another delivery and drinking to the poor corpses' health.

It would have stayed that way too, if Lo Khan hadn't done a favor for some friends of Shug's. Of course, these friends just happened to be high profile Rebel-types. This isn't the first time he's gotten grief over a favor, but with the *Marauder* blasted up and sitting in Impound, it may just be the last. Still, you don't last as long as Lo Khan has if you don't have connections. Lo Khan figures it won't be long until things get straightened out and the *Hyperspace Marauder* is once again cruising the starlanes.

■ The Hyperspace Marauder
Craft: TransGalMeg *Xiytiar*-class Transport
Type: Modified large transport
Scale: Capital
Length: 164.8 meters
Skill: Space transports: *Xiytiar*-class transport
Crew: 2
Crew Skill: See Lo Khan and Luwingo
Passengers: 12
Cargo Capacity: 5,000 metric tons
Consumables: 3 months
Cost: 800,000 credits
Hyperdrive Multiplier: x3
Hyperdrive Backup: x16
Nav Computer: Yes
Maneuverability: 0D
Space: 3
Hull: 2D+1
Shields: 2D
Sensors:
  Passive: 20/0D
  Scan: 35/1D+1
  Search: 40/3D
  Focus: 2/3D
Note: The *Hyperspace Marauder* has a custom-made multi-band computer interface antenna. With this, Luwingo has +3D to *computer programming* and *security* rolls when attempting to take over any opponent's shipboard computer. The antenna has a broadcast range of 500 meters; therefore, this tactic is only practical on attempted boarding actions or on a planet's surface.

Slave II

Interstellar bounty hunters are a mobile lot. Unlike the skip tracers or repo-thugs that haunt a single system or planet, those who rake in the big contracts go where the money is. Travelling from planet to planet, crossing sectors and territories in pursuit of their prey, they usually can't depend on the vagaries of luxury liners or shuttles. That is why most of them own their own ships. Some are innocuous little tramp shuttles, others are combat ships, and some qualify as cargo ships because they transport living, even if barely so, beings.

Boba Fett is reputed to be one of the most dangerous bounty hunters in the galaxy. The reason Fett is so dangerous is because he always plans ahead. Way ahead. That's why he has kept a backup ship for situations that require stealth or subterfuge. A bounty hunter can never have enough advantages as far as Fett is concerned, and that's why he had another ship ready to go should *Slave I* ever be severely damaged. Based on a Mandalorian police ship design, the *Slave II* is a less heavily armed ship, though that is a relative concept. To compensate, it is faster and more maneuverable than *Slave I*. Although it took Boba Fett quite a while to retrieve *Slave I* from the Alliance, he decided to use *Slave II* while on Nar Shaddaa — it was much easier to catch Solo and other potential quarry off-guard.

Boba Fett has been taking advantage of his "death" to get even with a lot of old enemies. To do this he needs to keep a low profile, which only *Slave II* can provide. While *Slave II* suffered quite a bit of damage after its encounter with Byss' planetary shield, it won't be long until Fett is after Solo again …

■ Slave II

Craft: MandalMotors *Pursuer* Enforcement Ship
Type: Modified Systems Patrol Vehicle
Scale: Starfighter
Length: 30.1 meters
Skill: Starfighter piloting: *Pursuer*
Crew: 1
Crew Skill: See Boba Fett
Passengers: 2, 5 (prison cells)

Back in Business

When the Alliance first confiscated the *Slave I*, no one really had any idea what to do with it. For one thing, there was a lockout code on the autopilot computer. Rebel staff had been able to get inside the ship and access the computers, but they couldn't fire up the engines. They ended up towing it to the Alliance's storage base on Grakouine. Given time, they could eventually crack the codes and the ship would be theirs.

Then what to do with it? The Alliance, flush with new legitimacy, had no need for a bounty hunter's ship. Skywalker, Organa, even Solo wanted nothing to do with it. Bad memories they said. Calrissian nearly had Voren Na'al sold on the idea of renting it out to carnivals before Admiral Ackbar nixed the idea. It sat untouched on Grakouine for months and, eventually, years. With other pressing matters, it was quietly forgotten.

The one person who still cared about it was Fett himself, convalescing from his encounter with the Sarlacc. Fett was wary of further contacts with Solo and his Jedi friend Skywalker. So he decided on a new tack: he'd buy the ship back legally. Of course, he couldn't do that without precautions, but he hadn't been doing jobs for galactic big shots without racking up an impressive list of favors.

Some credits in the right hands, a few comsignals to the right people, and he was ready to buy the ship as part of a "surplus liquidation" deal. Dummy corporations, fake IDs and forged requisition forms can be nearly as useful as a thermal detonator in the right circumstances. He got an old employer, Crystalboy, to do some of the middleman work and within weeks a familiar olive drab hulk was his, free and clear again.

Once *Slave I* was repaired and cleaned up, he took it and stored it in a parking orbit above Nar Shaddaa, where it floats waiting for its master to return. Fett has only begun to collect all that he feels he is owed.

Cargo Capacity: 35 metric tons
Consumables: 5 weeks
Cost: 225,000 credits
Hyperdrive Multiplier: x1
Hyperdrive Backup: x16
Nav Computer: Yes
Maneuverability: 1D
Space: 7
Atmosphere: 350; 1,000KMH
Hull: 5D
Shields: 1D
Sensors:
  Passive: 35/1D+1
  Scan: 55/2D+1
  Search: 80/3D+1
  Focus: 3/4D+1
Weapons:
  Twin Blaster Cannon (fire-linked)
    Fire Arc: Forward
    Skill: Starship gunnery
    Fire Control: 2D
    Space Range: 1-5/10/17
    Atmosphere Range: 100-500/1/1.7 KM
    Damage: 5D
  One Ion Cannon
    Fire Arc: Turret
    Skill: Starship gunnery
    Fire Control: 2D
    Space Range: 1-3/7/36
    Atmosphere Range: 50-100/200/500
    Damage: 8D
  One Proton Torpedo Launcher
    Fire Arc: Back
    Skill: Starship gunnery
    Fire Control: 3D+2
    Space Range: 1/3/7
    Atmosphere Range: 50-100/300/ 700
    Damage: 7D

Starfighters

Starfighters, or "snubfighters" as they are sometimes called, are small, normally one or two person, armed spacecraft. They have become an increasingly important part of warfare. A modern starfighter is a compact, highly maneuverable engine of destruction. Able to move at fantastic speeds, and sporting the most advanced modern weaponry and sensors, starfighters, once overlooked in strategic planning (note the Death Star's absolute inability to repel starfighter attacks), have been given increased value in modern tactics.

Starfighters can harass capital ships while other forces move into position, and can strafe ground emplacements and armies, demoralizing and disorganizing the most elite forces. They are now a vital part of military planning.

Some of the most dramatic technological advances of the past few years have occurred in the field of starfighter technology. New generations seem to be coming along every few years — it wasn't that long ago that a Z-95 Headhunter could hold its own under the right conditions. Now, it is simply a very fast coffin.

There have been three distinct generations of starfighters in the current era. The first was the arrival of the X-wing starfighter. This vehicle proved that starfighters could be a vital part of space combat and triggered the technological war that continues to this day. Next, the introduction of the B-wing, A-wing and TIE Interceptor signalled the coming of the second generation of modern fighters. The newest generation of starfighters has seen no less than four new fighter types: the A-9 Vigilance Interceptor, the Republic E-wing, the automated TIE/D and the Incom "Howlrunner." The arrival of the TIE/D is an ominous sign: its success at the Battle of Calamari will surely encourage the continued development of fully automated fighters, paving the way for untold destruction in future wars.

X-wing

Popularly known as the X-wing, the Incom T-65 was the mainstay of the Alliance's flying corps for over a decade. Designed by Rebel sympathizers in the Incom Corporation, the X-wing was an offshoot of the venerable Z-95 Headhunter. Combining maneuverability, speed and heavy armaments, it is one of the best multipurpose fighters ever designed and has served reliably over the years. Though the Republic has developed newer and faster designs, the X-wing still flies priority missions while other fighters, such as the sturdy Y-wing, are being phased out.

In addition to a highly efficient hyperdrive engine, there are beefed up blasters mounted on S-foils for better targeting. The X-wing saves on valuable space by incorporating an interface socket for an astromech unit. This allows the droid to perform in-flight repairs and still incorporate full astrogation systems and charts.

Part of what makes the X-wing so practical is its adaptability. It may never replace the airspeeder for atmospheric flight, but it can fight in a vacuum and then hit an atmosphere without serious performance drop-off. Alliance pilots are very loyal to the X-wing and Rogue Squadron, among others, have resisted the upgrade to new designs.

■ X-wing
  Craft: Incom T-65B X-wing
  Type: Space superiority fighter
  Scale: Starfighter
  Length: 12.5 meters
  Skill: Starfighter piloting: X-wing
  Crew: 1 and astromech droid (can coordinate)
  Crew Skill: Starfighter piloting 5D, starship gunnery 4D+2, starship shields 3D
  Cargo Capacity: 110 kilograms
  Consumables: 1 week
  Cost: 150,000 credits

Hyperdrive Multiplier: x1
Nav Computer: Uses astromech unit
Maneuverability: 3D
Space: 8
Atmosphere: 365; 1050KMH
Hull: 4D
Shields: 1D
Sensors:
  Passive: 25/0D
  Scan: 50/1D
  Search: 75/2D
  Focus: 3/4D
Weapons:
  Four Laser Cannons (fire-linked)
    Fire Arc: Front
    Skill: Starship gunnery
    Fire Control: 3D
    Space Range: 1-3/12/25
    Atmosphere Range: 100-300/1.2/2.5KM
    Damage: 6D
  Two Proton Torpedo Launchers
    Fire Arc: Front
    Skill: Starship gunnery
    Fire Control: 2D
    Space Range: 1/3/7
    Atmosphere Range: 30-100/300/700
    Damage: 9D

A-9 Vigilance Interceptor

Kuat Drive Yards has long been a major player in the Imperial war industry. Manufacturer of the Star Destroyer (and many other ships), KDY has long wanted a crack at the snubfighter market. As long as TIE fighters were the fighter of choice of Navy planners, there was little chance, but their project teams have had designs on the back burner for years. With the Mutiny, there was an increased demand for light combat craft and KDY began building their prime design, the A-9 Vigilance Interceptor.

The A-9 is a sleek, stripped down fighter. Like other Imperial models, it lacks both hyperdrive and shields to cut all extraneous mass. In addi-

tion, it pares down the hull and escape systems (Imperial ejection systems have become a joke to most pilots anyway). Reduced cockpit complexity makes the A-9 one of the easiest fighters to learn. The A-9 is a very small craft, trading off mass for maneuverability, making it popular with elite pilot corps. The fighter's weaponry incorporates twin laser cannon that can be fired independently or linked.

Of course, KDY never predicted its state-of-the-art design would end up in New Republic hands. The majority of their factories are usually franchised out to the local governors of poor planets. One such governor was Abam Tev. Running her factories like slave yards, with low pay and no safety precautions, she inadvertently inspired the first Rebel cells in her system. Finally tired of the deteriorating conditions, the workers revolted and allied with the New Republic, which was only too glad to accept the A-9 as well. The Republic has always preferred lightspeed capable fighters, but with a design this good, the compromise was worth it.

■ A-9 Vigilance Interceptor
  Craft: Kuat Drive Yards A-9 Vigilance Interceptor
  Type: Territorial defensive interceptor
  Scale: Starfighter
  Length: 7.4 meters
  Skill: Starfighter piloting: A-9
  Crew: 1
  Crew Skill: Starfighter piloting 4D+2, starship gunnery 4D+1
  Cargo Capacity: 55 kilograms
  Consumables: 1 day
  Cost: 185,000 credits
  Maneuverability: 4D+1
  Space: 12
  Atmosphere: 450; 1,300KMH
  Hull: 2D+2
  Sensors:
    Passive: 10/1D
    Scan: 35/2D+1
    Search: 60/3D+1
    Focus: 3/4D

STORMING DOWN OVER THE VAST CALAMARI OCEANS, PHALANXES OF NEW ALLIANCE *E-WINGS* TACKLE THE *WORLD SMASHERS* HEAD-ON!

KNAVE ONE TO KNAVE TEAM-- BLAST ANYTHING THAT LOOKS LIKE A *SCANNING TOWER*-- THAT'S THE KEY TO *VICTORY*!

The A-9 Vigilance Interceptor (foreground) and Republic E-wing (background)

Weapons:
Two Heavy Turbolaser Cannons (can be fire-linked)
Fire Arc: Front
Skill: Starship gunnery
Fire Control: 2D
Space Range: 1-3/12/25
Atmosphere Range: 100-300/1.2/2.5KM
Damage: 5D (6D when fire-linked)

E-wings

Once the Rebel Alliance depended upon preying upon unarmed Imperial shipments. Now, the situation is reversed. The Empire has increasingly preyed on Republic shipping and the Republic finds itself hard-pressed to defend its vessels from assault. To address this need, FreiTek, a company formed by the Incom designers who defected and brought the X-wing design with them to the Rebellion, has produced the E-wing.

The FreiTek E-wing is the first fighter designed and executed entirely under the auspices of the New Republic. Intended as a defensive interceptor, it is a heavy, combat dedicated ship. The vessel is akin to the B-wing and Y-wing designs: designed to take punishment and eager to dish it out. The vessel isn't pretty, but it can hold its own, and isn't nearly as prone to break down as the finicky B-wing. To simplify the design, FreiTek eliminated movable S-foils in favor of a fixed wing design, resulting in a more reliable and cheaper fighter (of course, the cost is still high because of the E-wing's impressive weaponry). A major breakthrough has been a totally redesigned hyperdrive interface. Developed in conjunction with Industrial Automaton, it uses the newly developed R7 astromech droid and is an attempt to recapture the success of the X-wing/R2 interfacing system.

From initial tests, the E-wing is a solid design and has performed well according to its pilots, with one exception. According to some, the weapons systems need some work. The original design used synthetically spin-coiled Tibanna gas. Most companies use natural spin-sealing methods, but with the state of the galactic economy, synthetics seemed an economical al-

SPEWING *HUNDREDS* OF THE SHINY NEW ATTACK SHIPS FROM ITS *MECHANICAL ENTRAILS*, THE GREAT *DEVASTATOR* PULLS AWAY FROM THE PLANET'S SURFACE --

THEY'VE HIT GREEN LEADER!

PULL OUT! PULL OUT!

ternative. Unfortunately, when exposed to the residual engine emissions, the gas's spiral structure breaks down, dramatically decreasing weapon range.

Ordinarily, Republic techs would just replace the artificially coiled gas, but this can take weeks. With the recent crisis at Calamari, there was no time to waste. The techs jury-rigged the weapons by tripling the power intake (an admittedly risky solution, but the only one short of grounding all E-wings for the duration). These models have been dubbed the "Type B" to distinguish them. So far, there have been no mishaps, but the technicians are hoping to solve the flaw before any pilots pay the price.

■ E-wing

Craft: FreiTek Inc. E-wing Starfighter: Type A
Type: Attack and close support fighter
Scale: Starfighter
Length: 11.2 meters
Skill: Starship Piloting: E-wing
Crew: 1
Crew Skill: Starfighter piloting 5D, starship gunnery 4D+2
Cargo Capacity: 110 kg
Consumables: 1 week
Cost: 185,000 credits
Hyperdrive Multiplier: x2
Nav Computer: Uses R7 astromech
Maneuverability: 3D+1
Space: 11
Atmosphere: 435; 1,300KMH
Hull: 5D
Shields: 1D
Sensors:
  Passive: 30/0D
  Scan: 55/1D
  Search: 85/2D+1
  Focus: 5/4D
Weapons:
  Triple Heavy Blaster Cannon (fire-linked)
    Fire Arc: Front
    Skill: Starship gunnery
    Fire Control: 3D+2
    Space Range: 1-3/5/8

■ The TIE/D in action against Republic X-wings over Calamari.

Atmosphere Range: 100-300/500/800
Damage: 6D
One Proton Torpedo Launcher
  Fire Arc: Front
  Skill: Starship gunnery
  Fire Control: 2D
  Space Range: 1/3/7
  Atmosphere Range: 30-100/300/700
  Damage: 9D

■ E-wing: Type B

Identical stats as the Type A except for:
  Triple Heavy Blaster Cannons (fire-linked)
    Fire Arc: Front
    Skill: Starship gunnery
    Fire Control: 3D+2
    Space Range: 1-5/10/25
    Atmosphere Range: 100-500/1/2.5KM
    Damage: 6D
Note: When a pilot rolls a mishap while firing the blaster cannon, roll on the table below:

1-3   Blaster cannon functions normally.

4   Blaster cannon shorts out for one round but can be repaired with a Very Easy *starship weapon repair* roll by R7 unit.

5   Blaster cannon burns out. Cannot be repaired in battle. With replacement parts, *starship weapon repair* difficulty is Moderate and takes one hour.

6   Blaster cannon will explode in 1D rounds doing 8D damage.

TIE/D Automated Fighter

An entirely automated military force has been a dream of Imperial planners for decades, but until recently, it was an impractical one. Recent advances in droid technology have finally made automated fighters a viable alternative to organic pilots, although performance still generally lags behind living opponents.

The advances came from the mind of General

STAR
WARS

Arndall Lott, who established his own private empire after the Battle of Endor (see *Wanted by Cracken* for more information). Inspired by the famed *Katana* fleet and its slave rigging hardware, his engineers eventually designed a reasonably reliable fully automated system. Lott's primitive prototype slave-rigged several vehicles together, which were controlled by a remote pilot; with his system, one pilot could control several AT-AT walkers. Of course, his system did have its liabilities: the computer system wasn't sophisticated enough to make the vehicles as efficient as organically piloted ones and the broadcasts were susceptible to jamming or odd energy emissions.

While the current automated systems mark a vast improvement over Lott's pioneer system, they are still far from perfect. The TIE/D fighters, first used in the Battle of Calamari, feature sophisticated onboard droid brains. The ships can fly as fully independent fighters with the droid brain, or be remotely controlled by computer-slaving systems. The Empire doesn't expect to fully deploy the TIE/D for many years: at current performance levels, TIE/Ds must normally use overwhelming numbers to defeat foes. Until the vessel can match the performance of an organic pilot, the TIE/Ds will remain a technological curiosity.

A flight of Incom I-7 Howlrunners prepare for a sortie on Coruscant.

TIE/D Automated Fighter
Craft: Sienar TIE/D Automated Starfighter
Type: Multi-environment automated attack fighter
Scale: Starfighter
Length: 6.1 meters
Crew: None (fully automated droid brain)
Consumables: 1 day
Cost: 170,000 credits
Maneuverability: 2D+1
Space: 10
Atmosphere: 450; 1300 KMH
Hull: 3D
Sensors:
  Passive: 20/1D
  Scan: 25/1D+2
  Search: 40/2D
  Focus: 2/3D
Weapons:
  Two Laser Cannon (fire-linked)
    Fire Arc: Front
    Skill: Starship gunnery
    Space Range: 1-3/12/25
    Atmosphere Range: 100-300/1.2/2.5KM
    Damage: 4D+2

Droid Brain
DEXTERITY 1D

KNOWLEDGE 1D
MECHANICAL 1D
Starfighter piloting 2D+2, starship gunnery 3D
PERCEPTION 1D
Search 4D
TECHNICAL 1D

Incom I-7 Howlrunner

The Incom Corporation is so famous for designing the T-65B X-wing, that people often forget that it was nationalized by the Empire. The I-7 Howlrunner is the first design from Incom since it was reorganized by the Empire, and while the company's legacy as a "Rebel" company hasn't endeared the Howlrunner to many Imperial pilots, those who view the design with an unbiased eye will admit that it is a quality product.

The Howlrunner is streamlined and is as effective in atmosphere as vacuum. It can be launched either from orbit or a ground base and can pursue enemies without any loss of performance. Named after a wild omnivorous predator native to the heat-baked sands of Kamar, the Howlrunner is famed for its tenacity and ferocity; Incom integrated these qualities into the fighter.

Few sorties have been fought between the I-7 and its predecessor, the X-wing, but military analysts on both sides are keen to see just how the current Incom designs stacks up against Incom's original X-wing.

Incom I-7 Howlrunner
Craft: Incom I-7 "Howlrunner"
Type: Multi-environment attack fighter

Scale: Starfighter
Length: 11.4 meters
Skill: Starfighter piloting: I-7
Crew: 1
Crew Skill: Starfighter piloting 4D, starship gunnery 4D+1
Cargo Capacity: 80 kilograms
Consumables: 2 days
Cost: 165,000 credits
Maneuverability: 3D+1
Space: 9
Atmosphere: 450; 1300KMH
Hull: 4D
Shields: 1D+1
Sensors:
  Passive: 20/0D
  Scan: 40/1D
  Search: 55/2D
  Focus: 3/3D
Weapons:
  Two Laser Cannon (fire-linked)
    Fire Arc: Front
    Skill: Starship gunnery
    Fire Control: 3D
    Space Range: 1-3/12/25
    Atmosphere Range: 100-300/1.2/2.5KM
    Damage: 5D+2

CloakShape Fighter

Kuat Systems Engineering's CloakShape fighter (or CS fighter) is an outdated space and atmospheric starfighter that still finds use on backwater worlds and in private arsenals. While it lacks the speed and offensive punch of more modern craft, the reinforced hull makes the vessel quite sturdy for a starfighter. CloakShapes still in service often find use as system patrol craft, smuggler blockade vessels and in anti-piracy support actions.

The fighters have respectable atmospheric performance, but their small powerplants make them unsuitable for deep space combat. The CloakShape is a surprisingly simple design — so much so that few ships still in service have gone unmodified. Modularized compartments and universal adaptors allow the ships to be fitted with virtually any aftermarket system: heavier weapons, larger fuel capacity, or more powerful thrusters. The most popular add-on is Curich Engineering's rear wing and stabilizer conversion kit; it is so common that few people realize they aren't part of the original fighter. These fins not only provide additional maneuverability, but allow a hyperdrive sled to be rigged into the CloakShape. Still, a CloakShape has its limitations, as amply shown by the one which pursued the *Millennium Falcon* over Nar Shadda. Like the Z-95, its relative slowness allows even heavy weapons, such as those in Shug's "chute," to target them with deadly accuracy.

■ CloakShape Fighter

Craft: Kuat Systems Engineering CloakShape Fighter
Type: Stock multi-purpose starfighter
Scale: Starfighter
Length: 15 meters
Skill: Starfighter piloting: CloakShape
Crew: 1
Crew Skill: Varies
Cargo Capacity: 40 kilograms
Consumables: 1 day
Cost: 15,000 credits (stock and used)
Maneuverability: 1D+1
Space: 6
Atmosphere: 330; 950KMH
Hull: 4D+2
Weapons:
  Double Laser Cannons (fire-linked)
    Fire Arc: Front
    Skill: Starship gunnery
    Fire Control: 1D+2
    Space Range: 1-5/10/17
    Atmosphere Range: 100-500/1KM/1.7KM
    Damage: 4D+2
  Dual Concussion Missile Launchers (fire-linked)
    Fire Arc: Front
    Skill: Missile weapons
    Fire Control: 2D
    Space Range: 1/3/7
    Atmosphere Range: 50-100/300/700
    Damage: 7D

■ Maneuvering Fin
Cost: 5,000 credits
Maneuverability: 2D+2

■ Hyperdrive Sled
Cost: 15,000 credits
Hyperdrive Multiplier: x3
Nav Computer: Uses R1 unit

Chapter Seven
The World Devastators

No sooner was the original Death Star destroyed than the Emperor, from his throne on Coruscant, decreed another should be built. Most who heard this mistook it for posturing: an attempt to deny the Rebel Alliance any satisfaction from their triumph. As time passed and appropriations charters arrived, they realized that he was all too serious.

Even as this second Death Star was being assembled, Umak Leth, Chief Engineer to the Emperor, came to his master with a new design for a molecular furnace that could break down the physical structure of matter. There had been devices of this type for years, on Coruscant in particular. On this ancient world, these machines razed older buildings, recycled the crumbling masonry and transparisteel, and left gleaming new spires in their places. The technology had also been incorporated into mining droids for many centuries. Leth's model was different. It had a much more sophisticated way of magnetically separating matter into constituent elements, then shaping them with sophisticated force beams and automata.

Pleased with this development, the Emperor agreed to fund further study with one caveat: a way must be found to harness this device to handle the industrial needs of the Empire. After months of work, Leth perfected a design concept that would take hold of an object with tractor beams and draw it into the molecular furnace. Shattering chemical bonds with intrinsic force negators, the materials could be stored in force bubbles of thallium, cadmium, impervium and other metals.

Presenting this idea to the Emperor, he was pleased with the reaction. The second Death Star project was proceeding well and plans were made for the Emperor to personally supervise its completion. Palpatine gave specific orders to begin work on a weapons platform to be constructed around the molecular furnace. It was to be self-sustaining and capable of enormous destruction.

In funding Leth's project, Palpatine cleverly exploited his engineer's ambition to exceed the great Bevel Lemelisk. Since he replaced Lemelisk as Master of Imperial Projects, he craved the opportunity to make a lasting mark of his own; the shadow of Lemelisk's Death Star had to be overcome. To succeed where the Death Star had failed would be quite an achievement and earn him a place in Imperial history. In doing so, he was also fulfilling long held and secret plans of the Emperor himself.

Of course, the Emperor's presumed death might have been expected to slow the work or kill the project outright. But, armed with irrevocable funding writs, Leth was determined to see just how far his talent could take him. No matter the cost.

The Design

The amount of coordination needed to run and maintain a World Devastator's myriad functions is a challenge to the most able crew. Rather than rely on countless individual droids, Leth opted for a sole high-functioning droid brain, reaching a level of automation unparalleled in any previous Imperial vessel. Even the Old Republic had never created a vehicle of this level of complexity. A new generation of highly advanced computers handled the major functions of the World Devastators.

The secret of these titanic weapons is that they are not vehicles in the traditional sense at all. All higher systems, like life support and defense, function in the same manner as standard Imperial craft, with weapons crewed by organics. However, the factories and production systems are controlled by artificially intelligent computer brains. The World Devastators are enormous droids; the crew, technicians and slaves live in special compartments inside. They perform the programming and feed information to the central brains, but once this is done, the Devastators operate freely within their designated parameters.

(The following textfile is taken from the notes of a recent guest lecture given by Arhul Hextrophon at Brionelle Memorial Military Academy on Chandrila shortly after the attack on Calamari.)

"A persistent question for New Republic strategists has been the seemingly endless Imperial obsession with super weapons. From Super Star Destroyers to torpedo spheres, it has been nearly impossible to overestimate the amount of destructive force available to the average Moff or Sector Group Commander. The Imperial Star Fleet has thousands of capital ships with enough firepower to raze civilizations and sterilize worlds. Even at their mightiest, at the Battle of Endor, the combined fleets of the Rebel Alliance always relied on superior intelligence, guerrilla tactics and faith in the Force for victory.

"The military planners of the New Order have an insatiable appetite for newer and deadlier weapons. The most famous of these weapons, and most characteristic of the Imperial mind, have been the Death Stars.

"Immense, seemingly impregnable and armed with a numbing amount of destructive power, including the famed superlaser, Death Stars are the ultimate weapon. Still, they have proven surprisingly vulnerable to attack. After the one-in-a-trillion shot that blew the first Death Star to atoms in the Yavin system, Imperial propaganda departments went into overdrive. Better to deny the station ever existed than suggest the almighty Empire could suffer such a staggering defeat. The last few reports from Alderaan were too panicked to be reliable and with the Empire's control of the media, it was quite easy for the Empire to stem the flow of information. It was easy enough for the surviving witnesses (mainly Rebel Alliance members) to be discredited or eliminated.

"The truly surprising aspect of the matter was the fact that the Empire immediately began work on a second Death Star after the first was destroyed. The Endor system was chosen as the construction site. This time, the Emperor saw to it that word of the project reached his enemies — this new Death Star would serve as bait for a massive trap. Against all odds, this new version of 'the ultimate weapon in the galaxy' was destroyed by Alliance warriors.

"Logically, that should have destroyed all faith in the Tarkin Doctrine. And yet we can see this is not so. Shortly before the attack on Calamari, the Rebellion received reports of fringe worlds in the Borderland Regions whose surfaces had been burned away by monstrous things the survivors called 'city-smashers.'

"Of course, we eventually learned the truth of these stories. The horrible World Devastators were simply the latest of the Empire's super weapons.

"By closely examining the Tarkin Doctrine itself, we can find an explanation for the continued development of super weapons. To quote:

'— it has long been my contention that your New Order needs one undeniable and overwhelming symbol to impress and, yes, frighten the masses ...'

"The key word is 'symbol.' We can see from this that the Death Star was never required to function to be effective. That it did was a great bonus, but largely irrelevant. In more ways than one, the original Death Star had already served much of its purpose by the time it was destroyed.

"It could paralyze whole worlds with fear. Where there was one, why not more? In the imagination of the public, there lurked the fear that some similar weapon remained, or perhaps even a fleet of them hidden in some dark region of space, striking secretly against intransigent worlds. The secrecy that had always surrounded the project and the vehemence with which the existence of the Death Star was denied by the Empire gave it the power of a mythic symbol.

"Damned good propaganda. Yet there is evidence to suggest that there is more to the Tarkin Doctrine than was first believed. With the revelation of the Emperor's possible immortality, a new theory comes to mind. With seemingly no end to his reign, the Emperor could foresee a time when he would want to expand his reign.

"Would a single galaxy be enough for Palpatine the Undying? I think not. The Old Republic had long considered the possibility of contact with other galaxies and made several abortive attempts at it. Palpatine had even secretly destroyed the most recent of these, the Outbound Flight project. According to what we have retrieved from Admiral Thrawn's notes, he led the mission to kill the six Jedi aboard the ship.

"It seems obvious that Palpatine's ultimate goal was the conquest, not just of our galaxy, but of others. What better way to ensure his military supremacy than with these World Devastators? Arriving at world after world, consuming and creating weapons while the battle rages on about them, never lacking for resources or energy ... the thought is terrifying.

"We must be thankful that the efforts of our bravest heroes, especially Luke Skywalker and Leia Organa Solo, have ended the Emperor's terror."

When armed and shielded, a World Devastator would be virtually immune to attack. Even as the enemy threw their resources at it, it would take them up and devise new weapons to hurl at its targets.

The first such Devastator, the *Silencer-1*, began construction in secret at the newly reopened shipyard in orbit around Thomork. Closed years ago because of a new strain of contagious hive virus, the system had taken on the dark reputation of a massacre site. The Emperor's agents had to kill over 450 people to make their story hold, but the area was soon as infamous as the fabled Dagobah system. In fact, the whole station was undamaged and, with the colony abandoned, perfect for a top secret project such as this.

The Master Control Signal

Considering the awesome destructive capability of these weapons, they would be a formidable threat if one were to go haywire or fall into enemy hands. Some previous Imperial combat droids had done just that. One memorable example was an assassin droid that killed most of the audience at a swoop tournament while pursuing a single target (this incident led to assassin droids being "officially" outlawed). Obviously, precautions had to be taken. Therefore, a special coded override circuit, the Master Control Signal, is hardwired into the main system computer of each World Devastator.

This circuit responds only to a special HoloNet hyperchannel frequency originating from Byss. This Master Control Signal utilizes new HoloNet frequencies and is broadcast at all times. It is responsible for coordinating the functions of all the Devastators in a single battlegroup.

The Master Control Signal is the most highly guarded secret in the entire Imperial arsenal because with it one can override all commands from the bridge. In case of emergency, it is possible to temporarily shut down the entire mechanism long enough for repairs to be made.

Of course, the Master Control Signal was the downfall of the Empire at Calamari. Luke Skywalker retrieved the codes for the Rebellion, and R2-D2 was able to command the World Devastators to shut down and turn their weapons upon each other.

Construction

While standardization and interchangeability are hallmarks of Imperial technology policy, the World Devastator is unique among Imperial war machines in that no two of them are identical. This is because they are not assembled by droids and techs: they assemble themselves. In effect, they build themselves while in operation.

All World Devastators begin as virtually identical machines. They have a basic brain core, although individual machines may have specialized programming for specific functions. Each World Devastator has sensor webs, factory maintenance subsystems and cognitive defensive subroutines. Once these powerful processors are brought on line, they are attached to the fabrication units and molecular furnaces.

The fabrication units include machining scanners, robotic lathes and automated assembly lines to turn the raw materials into weapons, droids and combat vehicles. The computer and the initial fabrication units are supported by a framework, called an endoskeleton, which determines the Devastator's final shape. The molecular furnace and its attendant software, which is responsible for breaking down raw materials, is also attached to the endoskeleton in the initial construction phase.

Once the endoskeleton is assembled, the proto-Devastator is allowed to run under supervision for a few weeks. Fed a steady supply of slag metals and raw ores, it atomizes them all and begins churning out parts, including additional body sections, weapons for the Devastator and larger assembly lines. While the endoskeletons of all Devastators look identical during this early phase, subtle differences become apparent as the machines build themselves.

After the first stages of construction, the World Devastator is normally only a few hundred meters at a side; it is in its "adolescence." The World Devastator will now be sent into battle, where all further development will occur.

At this stage, the Devastators are at their most vulnerable. The new machines attack in groups to maximize battle effectiveness and gather enough materials to increase their size and produce vehicles, starships and other vital weapons. This is where the self-improvement programming comes into play. The longer a Devastator functions, the more it improves and modifies itself, growing larger and more lethal.

As individual units grow larger, the battle squadron splits into smaller and smaller groups. Theoretically, a single Devastator could eventually become large enough to strip a planet unaided in a few weeks or even days. Neither Umak Leth nor his technicians have any idea what the upper limit to a Devastator's growth is.

Functions

Perhaps nothing so characterized the nature of Palpatine's New Order as much as the Tarkin Doctrine. It is still one of the underlying principles by which the Empire governs. While both

Death Stars were destroyed, this in no way invalidates the Tarkin Doctrine that spawned them. The World Devastator actually improves its effectiveness by virtue of its self-contained nature. Cannibalizing what it needs and refining the materials to make new vehicles and fighters, Devastators are excellent weapons. The amount of time it takes to lay waste to a planet may be quite long compared to the instantaneous destruction of a planet with the superlaser, but the World Devastator wastes nothing.

Raw materials are molecularized and siphoned off to the fabrication plants deep in the bellies of these behemoth constructs. Subsidiary computers hold design specifications for dozens of different robot fighters, battlespeeders and automated tanks. Based on priorities assigned by the commander, the master technicians set production levels and assembly schedules. With so many interconnected computer systems, a realignment of assembly priorities can take several hours. Once the computers have the designs on-line, the great internal factories can begin working on the fabrication.

As the first of the elements and alloys are channelled by force field into the forming chambers, they are shaped and formed, molded by robot manipulators and welded, cut, stamped and tooled into the necessary parts. The parts are then moved to the assembly lines, where droids, workers and slaves begin assembling the new machines to correspond to the selected patterns.

The two most important individuals in the onboard factories are the Calibration Engineer, who maintains the furnace temperature and force field siphons, and the Assembly Commander, who must oversee the actual production to peak efficiency.

During a battle situation, the commander may either rely on the built-in turbolasers, ion cannons or other weapons, or he may begin charging up the battle craft the Devastator manufactures. Many of these are automated craft that are controlled by combat technicians from the bridge. Alternatively, the Devastators work in tandem with heavily armored military transports that ferry the many pilots and crewmembers necessary to operate any manned vehicles that are built. The World Devastator uses a series of tractor beam projectors to direct materials into the maw of the molecular furnace, which has a layer of plasma shields around it to protect the World Devastator itself.

The sun-hot maw of the molecular furnace at the front, bottom or rear of a World Devastator can break down any structure, from bare mountainside to starship to gleaming city. Even starships aren't immune to the effect, as demonstrated by the fate of the Rebel Star Destroyer *Emancipator*. World Devastators can also devour barren planetoids and asteroids, destroyed vehicles and ships or any other source of metals, plastics and other components.

Depending on the mineral wealth of the victim planet, the World Devastator's factories may create a surplus of finished goods; these are shipped to other warships or industrial worlds for processing. The World Devastators are not currently capable of reproducing the computer cores and fabrication equipment it takes to make more Devastators, but in time, even that problem could be surmounted.

Structure

While the specific layout of each Devastator is different, there are certain features common to all of them. The control bridge, usually located on the top of the Devastator, houses the centralized computers in a command module. The upper three levels are usually arranged as quarters and recreation areas for the commander, his crew and all troops and technicians aboard the vessel.

The main computer cortex is directly attached to the endoskeleton, underneath the command module and living quarters. The cortex is at the heart of the endoskeleton, which stretches between the four support and thruster columns, which house the sublight and hyperspace engines. The central computer core occupies nearly 20 levels, with additional minor computing stations (for various functions) scattered throughout the vehicle, including at each weapon emplacement, on the assembly lines and at the molecular furnaces.

The various assembly lines, hangars, armories and power cores are built around the computer core and placed throughout new levels. The interior of each World Devastator is unique, so exact placement of components varies from machine to machine.

All levels directly above the computer cortex will remain unchanged as the machine modifies itself. However, as the machine grows, additional customized levels are added below and behind the computer core — what results is a thoroughly unique war machine.

When materials are funneled through the molecular furnaces, the molten materials travel into the separation lattices. Selective ionizing grids filter specific elements and particles out and condense and purify them. The materials are then cooled and stored in force field spheres (which can be transferred to cargo ships) or

"AS YOU CAN SEE, THE DEVASTATORS CONSUME *EVERYTHING* IN THEIR PATH..."

"...IN THEIR HOLDS GREAT *FURNACES* AND *FACTORIES* PROCESS THE CATACLYSMIC FEAST INTO RAW ELEMENTS... AND NEW *WEAPONS OF DESTRUCTION!*"

transferred directly to the fabricators. Finished goods are hauled up to storage areas adjacent to launching decks and hangar bays.

Overall, the World Devastators are among the most devastating weapons ever created by the Empire. They combine the horrors of modern weaponry with the efficiency of mass production, giving the Empire almost unlimited potential for weapons manufacture.

Silencer-7

The *Silencer-7* was the lead attack vehicle in the Battle of Calamari and represented the first major command of Titus Klev. It was destroyed in the final stages of the battle, a victim of R2-D2's commands. Almost all hands aboard were lost and the wreck remains at the bottom of Calamari's ocean.

◼ Silencer-7
Craft: World Devastator
Type: Planetary assault weapon
DEXTERITY 1D
KNOWLEDGE 1D
Planetary systems 7D
MECHANICAL 4D
Astrogation 8D, capital ship gunnery 6D, capital ship piloting 6D, capital ship shields 6D, repulsorlift operation 8D, space transports 5D, starship gunnery 5D, starship shields 5D, World Devastator operation 5D
PERCEPTION 1D
Search 6D
STRENGTH 1D
TECHNICAL 6D
Computer programming/repair 8D, droid construction 7D, droid engineering (A) 6D, droid programming 8D, droid repair 8D, repulsorlift construction 6D, repulsorlift construction 8D, repulsorlift engineering (A) 3D, repulsorlift repair 9D, security 6D, walker construction 6D, walker engineering (A) 4D, walker repair 9D

Scale: Capital
Length: 3,200 meters, 1,500 meters tall
Skill: World Devastator operation
Crew: 23,684, gunners: 1,975, skeleton: 4,209/+10, slaves: 2,000, droids: 1,600
Crew Skill: Astrogation 3D+1, capital ship gunnery 4D, capital ship shields 5D, World Devastator operation 6D
Passengers: 8,803 (troops), 1,500 (pilots)
Cargo Capacity: 49,000 metric tons
Consumables: 2 years*
* Consumables may be considerably extended because the World Devastators can break down and reconstitute various elements.
Cost: Not available for sale
Hyperdrive Multiplier: x6
Hyperdrive Backup: x20
Nav Computer: Yes
Space: 5
Atmosphere: 140; 400KMH
Hull: 8D+1
Shields: 4D+1
Sensors:
Passive: 55/1D
Scan: 125/3D+1
Search: 250/4D
Focus: 6/4D+2
Weapons:
125 Heavy Turbolaser Batteries
Fire Arc: 50 front, 25 left, 25 right, 25 back
Crew: 3
Skill: Capital ship gunnery
Fire Control: 4D
Space Range: 3-15/30/75
Atmosphere Range: 300-600/1KM/2KM
Damage: 5D
200 Blaster Cannons
Fire Arc: 50 front, 50 left, 50 right, 50 back
Crew: 5
Scale: Starfighter
Skill: Starship gunnery
Fire Control: 2D
Space Range: 1-5/10/17
Atmosphere Range: 100-500/1/1.7KM
Damage: 8D
80 Proton Missile Tubes
Fire Arc: 20 front, 20 left, 20 right, 20 back
Crew: 6
Skill: Capital ship gunnery
Fire Control: 1D
Space Range: 1-2/8/15
Atmosphere Range: 100-200/800/1.5KM
Damage: 8D
15 Ion Cannons
Fire Arc: 5 front, 5 left, 5 right
Crew: 6
Skill: Capital ship gunnery
Fire Control: 2D+2
Space Range: 1-7/12/25
Atmosphere Range: 200-1.4/2.5/5KM
Damage: 3D
15 Tractor Beam Emplacements (front beams can be fire-linked)
Fire Arc: 10 front, 2 left, 2 right, 1 back
Crew: 10
Skill: Capital ship gunnery
Fire Control: 4D
Space Range: 1-5/15/30
Atmosphere Range: 200-1/3/6KM
Damage: 6D

Inquisitor-4

The *Inquisitor-4* is typical of new World Devastators that have just entered combat conditions. They are smaller and less well armed, but nonetheless make formidable foes. While it would be a secondary ship in a battlegroup like the one attacking Calamari, it might very well be the lead ship attacking a smaller, less defended planet.

■ Inquisitor-4
Craft: World Devastator
Type: Planetary assault weapon
DEXTERITY 1D
KNOWLEDGE 1D
Planetary systems 5D
MECHANICAL 3D
Astrogation 4D+2, capital ship gunnery 5D+1, capital ship piloting 5D, capital ship shields 5D, repulsorlift operation 4D, space transports 5D, starship gunnery 5D, starship shields 5D, World Devastator operation 4D
PERCEPTION 1D
Search 6D
STRENGTH 1D
TECHNICAL 3D+1
Computer programming/repair 5D+1, droid construction 5D, droid engineering (A) 4D, droid programming 8D, droid repair 8D, repulsorlift construction 5D, repulsorlift engineering (A) 3D+2, repulsorlift repair 8D, security 4D+1
Scale: Capital
Length: 1,700 meters, 900 meters tall
Skill: World Devastator operation
Crew: 21,640, gunners: 1,020, skeleton: 3,880/+10, slaves: 1,800, droids: 1,211
Crew Skill: Astrogation 3D, capital ship gunnery 4D, capital ship shields 4D, World Devastator operation 5D
Passengers: 6,700 (troops), 1,000 (pilots)
Cargo Capacity: 31,500 metric tons
Consumables: 2 years*
* Consumables may be considerably extended because the World Devastators can break down and reconstitute various elements.
Cost: Not available for sale
Hyperdrive Multiplier: x6
Hyperdrive Backup: x 20
Nav Computer: Yes
Space: 4
Atmosphere: 80; 230KMH
Hull: 6D+2
Shields: 3D+2
Sensors:
Passive: 50/1D
Scan: 100/3D
Search: 200/4D
Focus: 6/4D+2
Weapons:
80 Heavy Turbolaser Batteries
Fire Arc: 30 front, 15 left, 15 right, 20 back
Crew: 3
Skill: Capital ship gunnery
Fire Control: 4D
Space Range: 3-15/36/75
Atmosphere Range: 300-600/1KM/2KM
Damage: 5D
80 Blaster Cannons
Fire Arc: 30 front, 20 left, 20 right, 10 back
Crew: 5
Scale: Starfighter

Foreboding Conclusions

(The following is extracted from a Top Secret Intelligence memo from Brigadier Colin Darkmere, Intelligence Operations Command, to the Provisional Council of the New Republic.)

Fortunate as we have been to see the World Devastators finally defeated, there are some unpleasant realities that still confront us about their development and implementation. The stolen Master Control Signal has been most effective in overcoming the few surviving Devastators and no new attacks have occurred in at least a week.

However, this does not rule out the possibility that a modified coding system could be thrown against us. I have assigned a team to develop new counter-strategies. I doubt we have heard the end of the city-smashers.

The point I wish to address primarily is the aftermath, and what plans the Empire may still have for us. According to recently intercepted transmissions, there is a 64% increase in inter-sector communications. A unified front may be forming against us. This suggests that, before his latest (and, hopefully, permanent) demise, the Emperor, through proxies or by decree, galvanized his servants into a new level of coordination.

Militarily, we still hold the winning hand and most likely they realize this. Therefore, it is likely they will bide their time, sounding us out for weaknesses. Of greater concern is the possibility they may be preparing a newer, more fearsome weapon to throw against us. I have three field operations teams at work commanded by Captain Kushone, Commander Daclo Koat-xi and Colonel Keltric. Our web of informers backs up the conclusions we have come to:

1. The Empire is developing newer and more horrible weapons of mass destruction. Chief Engineer Umak Leth, among others, is working on them.

2. These weapons are still uncompleted. It is unknown how soon they might be brought into the conflict.

3. *Some* of these weapons are being developed in a high security research facility of which we are unaware. Leth and some of his staff have disappeared from our attention on at least eight occasions.

4. It is currently unknown how they have managed to keep this base totally hidden from our spies, but we are checking every clue to locate it.

The facts are few, and they are not at all comforting. This is all I can confidently present at this time, but I will apprise you as things develop. My strongest recommendation is to maintain a high level of readiness along our borders with the Empire until we learn more.

Skill: Starship gunnery
Fire Control: 2D
Space Range: 1-5/10/17
Atmosphere Range: 100-500/1/1.7KM
Damage: 6D

30 Proton Missile Tubes
Fire Arc: 15 front, 5 left, 5 right, 5 back
Crew: 6
Skill: Capital ship gunnery
Fire Control: 1D
Space Range: 1-2/8/15
Atmosphere Range: 100-200/800/1.5KM
Damage: 8D

10 Tractor Beam Emplacements
Fire Arc: 6 front, 2 left, 2 right
Crew: 10
Skill: Capital ship gunnery
Fire Control: 4D
Space Range: 1-5/15/30
Atmosphere Range: 200-1/3/6KM
Damage: 6D

STAR WARS

Chapter Eight
Vehicles

There are as many different types of vehicles as there are possible uses for them. From airspeeders, to swoops, to sail barges, there are countless models, variants and modifications for any expected vehicle use. There are many forms of propulsion, from the common repulsorlift, to fuel burning combustion engines to fusion. Likewise, the purpose of a given vehicle can vary dramatically, from fast, light combat assault vehicle to heavy duty cargo transport. *Dark Empire* introduces countless new vehicles, giving a glimpse into the latest in cutting edge technology and its uses on the modern battlefield.

Speeder Transports

Airspeeders can be crucial to a base's survival or victory in battle, but they are difficult to transport from world to world. Many New Republic airspeeders, like the T-47s, are pre-fabricated and shipped in parts. Once a new base is established, they are unpacked, checked and assembled. Come time to evacuate or regroup, the speeders usually have to be stripped, cleaned and taken apart. In the Battle of Hoth, the snowspeeders had been in running condition for less than a week when they were thrown into battle against the Empire's AT-ATs. Snubfighters would have been much more effective against the walkers by virtue of their superior firepower, but they were necessary as escorts for the evacuating transports. As is well known, the Rebels were able to evacuate, but the T-47s, due to lack of an appropriate transport, had to be left behind. These speeders could have been put to crucial use on other bases.

Clearly there had to be a new approach to transporting speeders across stellar distances. Obviously, converting them to spaceships was impossible. Any capital ship has more than enough room to haul a whole squadron, but speeders are useless when in too high an orbit. Any existing ship big enough to haul airspeeders

was too slow to quickly bring them into battle.

Realizing a need for a quick method of delivering a squadron of airspeeders to and from bases under fire, designers from Slayn & Korpil, makers of the B-wing, hit upon a radical idea. This idea was to make a two part system: a practical, all environment airspeeder and an interface transport to haul the speeders from capital ship bays. The result was the V-wing Transport/Combat Speeder team.

The V-wings are fueled and armed while still aboard the capital ship. The pilots board the V-wing transport (since the V-wings themselves are not sealed for spaceflight). The transport launches and dives through the atmosphere while snubfighters provide cover. While droids perform final calculations, the pilots enter their speeders through retractable docking sleeves.

Once preflight checks are finished, they fire up the engines and detach. As soon as all speeders have separated, the fighter escort and the transport move away — often the fighters engage in battle, while the transport returns to the capital ship for another group of speeders or maintains a distant orbit waiting for the pick-up rendezvous for the V-wings.

The transport/speeder combination has worked flawlessly in over a dozen battles, giving unprecedented mobility and first strike power. The original transport models hold four, while an updated model holds six speeders. Slayn & Korpil is working on a universal adapter to fit T-47s and other airspeeder models.

■ Speeder Transport
Craft: Slayn & Korpil V-wing Speeder Transport, Model A
Type: Orbital Interface Transport
Scale: Starfighter
Length: 20 meters
Skill: Space transports: V-wing transport
Crew: 2, skeleton: 1/+5
Crew Skill: Space transports 5D, starship shields 4D
Passengers: 4 (pilots)
Cargo Capacity: 2 metric tons (internal), docking sleeves for 4 V-wings
Consumables: 3 days

REBEL PILOTS, THEIR SKILLS HONED BY YEARS OF RELENTLESS WARFARE, SWOOP UNERRINGLY TOWARD THE FLOATING CALAMARI CITIES -- AND THE DEADLY *WORLD DEVASTATORS!*

EMANCIPATOR, THIS IS GREEN LEADER...WE'RE IN OPEN FORMATION AND STINGING HARD!

Cost: 175,000 credits
Maneuverability: 1D+2
Space: 4
Atmosphere: 350; 1,000KMH
Hull: 5D
Shields: 2D

■ Speeder Transport, Model B

The Model B is identical to the Model A with the following modifications:
Craft: Slayn & Korpil V-wing Speeder Transport, Model B
Length: 27 meters
Passengers: 6 (pilots)
Cargo Capacity: 4 metric tons (internal), docking sleeves for 6 V-wings
Cost: 195,000 credits

V-wing Airspeeder

Combat airspeeders fill an important niche in strategic planning. They are much simpler than comparable starfighters, and correspondingly cheaper as well. They are designed to work in atmospheres and their streamlining can give them more maneuverability and speed than many snubfighters despite less powerful engines.

Of course, speeders trade off safety for those vital performance factors. One good hit from a walker's guns is enough to vaporize most speeders. Even with excellent ejection devices, few pilots will last long against heavy fire. Speeders are excellent for guerrilla strikes and hit-and-run tactics, and often support ground forces and artillery.

The V-wing is the first of a new generation of combat airspeeder used by the Alliance. Drawing on years of experience, New Republic technicians have built a sleek lifting body with a difference. The whole shape is molded to channel the surrounding air into a Chab-Ylwoum scramjet intake. When the pilot cuts in afterburners, the scramjet greatly increases speed for a few crucial seconds. Though more difficult to handle while the scramjet is operational, its speed can give a pilot the edge to outrun or outfight an opponent.

The V-wing was already in the design stage when its manufacturer decided to create the speeder/transport system. So far, the V-wing has distinguished itself and it is expected to be an integral part of the Republic's defense forces for years to come.

■ V-wing Airspeeder

Craft: Slayn & Korpil V-wing Airspeeder
Type: Combat speeder
Scale: Speeder
Length: 6.3 meters
Skill: Repulsorlift operation: V-wing
Crew: 1
Crew Skill: Repulsorlift operation 5D, vehicle blasters 5D
Cargo Capacity: 15 kilograms
Cover: Full
Altitude Range: Ground level–50 kilometers; 51–99 kilometers, -1D maneuverability
Cost: 26,500 credits
Maneuverability: 3D
Move: 350; 1,000 KMH, scramjet: 485; 1,400KMH, but add +10 to all difficulties, can only be used for one round per minute
Body Strength: 3D+2
Weapons:
    Double Blaster Cannon (fire-linked)
      Fire Arc: Front
      Skill: Vehicle blasters
      Fire Control: 1D
      Range: 50-400/1KM/2KM
      Damage: 5D+1

Imperial Patrol Vehicles

Imperial policy has generally precluded the use of airspeeders in combat roles. Despite the New Order and its restructuring of the Navy and Army, much of the mindset behind the traditional roles in war have remained. During attacks, there is still a preference for orbital bombardments. During ground engagements, walkers and landspeeders take the majority of the task upon themselves. Even the Imperial Scouts prefer the stealth of a speeder bike to a larger, more heavily armed craft. There are, of course, situations when air power is necessary, and there, as with any use of force, the Empire will not shirk. TIE fighters and bombers are called

into service and, while at a slight disadvantage, perform well.

Still, there are situations where airspeeders are indispensable, and as one would expect, the Empire has vehicles appropriate for the situation. There are two main classifications of Imperial security vehicles: patrol craft and pursuit craft. A typical example is the *Guardian*-class patrol ship. Designed as a counter-insurgent observation craft, the Guardian can be spotted floating serenely over the kilometers-tall spires of the huge urban planets of the Core.

Unlike many other Imperial ships, this patrol cruiser's mission is to observe instead of confront. Equipped with extensive monitoring scanners and probescopes, they monitor the air traffic with precision. Randomly assigned routes allow a few hundred of them to blanket the entire surface of Byss every few hours if necessary. But this is not their only function, since there are many other spy devices at the Emperor's command.

Each Guardian functions as a mobile coordinating station for several dozen Hunter-Killer Probots. Should one of the HKs cease functioning, a patrol ship can be on the scene in minutes to assess the situation, while assigning other HKs as backup. Should something prove amiss, the crew can then signal to the garrison or command tower for more extensive support. Once this is done, the Guardian can function as a fully equipped forward observation site, relaying tactical information and intelligence.

These ships are highly sought throughout the Empire's military forces, but the majority of them have been assigned to Imperial Intelligence. Occasionally they are disguised as simple freighters and use this anonymity to spy on enemies. Ships of this type have even more elaborate equipment like lifeform scanners, spatial anomaly detectors and the like. However, the vehicle is not entirely defenseless: it has left and right-underside mounted blaster cannon that can be fire-linked or fired separately. If fire-linked, they must fire in the forward fire arc; if fired separately, the pilot handles the left/front blaster cannon, while the co-pilot handles the right/forward blaster cannon.

■ Guardian Patrol Ship

Craft: Tion Mil/Sci Industries *Guardian*-class Patrol Ship XL-5
Type: Orbital and upper atmospheric patrol vessel
Scale: Speeder
Length: 40 meters
Skill: Repulsorlift operation: XL-5 Guardian
Crew: 2
Crew Skill: Repulsorlift operation 4D, vehicle blasters 5D
Passengers: 12 (prisoners)
Cargo Capacity: 150 metric tons

Cover: Full
Altitude Range: Ground level–100 kilometers
Cost: 80,000 credits
Maneuverability: 1D
Move: 280; 800KMH
Body Strength: 3D
Shields: 3D
Sensors:
 Passive: 4KM/1D
 Scan: 8KM/2D
 Search: 20KM/3D
 Focus: 500/4D
Weapons:
 Two Blaster Cannon (fire-link optional)
  * All fire-linked stats are listed in ().
  Fire Arc: 1 left/front, 1 right/front (front)
  Crew: left/front: pilot, right/front: co-pilot (co-pilot)
  Skill: Vehicle blasters
  Fire Control: 1D (1D+2)
  Range: 50-400/900/3KM
  Damage: 4D (5D+1)

Storm Skimmer Patrol Sled

The storm skimmer patrol sled is an older weapon that has been reactivated with the decline of the Empire. The patrol sled was originally designed for use by scout troopers and was very popular nearly a decade ago — the image of a pair of stalwart troopers speeding to their duty on a patrol sled was a common sight in the media. Eventually, the sleds were replaced by the speeder bike, but the Empire kept a huge backorder of them as all-purpose vehicles.

With Imperial forces running dangerously short of weapons and vehicles, the Imperials were very careful in assigning troops. This was especially important on worlds with a sizable Rebel presence: often, seemingly minor incidents were used as Rebel feint maneuvers to lure out the Empire's heavy vehicles and leave vulnerable sites unprotected. To counter this, patrol sleds have been brought back into service to allow a small number of troops to respond rapidly to the first hint of unrest, before an incident can explode into violence.

Like the bikes that replaced them, patrol sleds have very limited weaponry in favor of speed and stealth. However, unlike the bikes, they offer a considerable amount of protection from enemy fire. The patrol sled is intended as a rapid deployment, antipersonnel craft; recent upgrades include a secondary repeating blaster

so multiple targets can be covered. Still, the sled is intended more as a deterrent rather than a full combat vehicle.

■ Storm Skimmer Patrol Sled

Craft: Uulshos Storm Skimmer Patrol Sled
Type: Atmospheric patrol vehicle
Scale: Speeder
Length: 4.6 meters
Skill: Repulsorlift operation: storm skimmer
Crew: 2
Crew Skill: Vehicle blasters 4D+1, repulsorlift operation 4D+2
Cargo Capacity: 100 kilograms
Cover: 1/2
Altitude Range: Ground level–10 kilometers; 11–15 kilometers, -1D maneuverability
Cost: 22,500 credits
Maneuverability: 2D+1
Move: 150; 430 KMH
Body Strength: 1D+2
Weapons:
 2 Heavy Repeating Blasters
  Fire Arc: 1 front, 1 left/front/right*
  * May turn to one facing per round
  Crew: Pilot: front, co-pilot: left/front/right
  Skill: Vehicle blasters
  Fire Control: 1D
  Range: 3-75/200/500 meters
  Damage: 5D+1

TIE Tanks

The coming of the New Republic brought liberty to thousands of worlds across the galaxy, but not always in the same way. For example, in the Tion, the citizens of Lianna jumped at the opportunity to declare themselves an independent, non-aligned world. For the first time in centuries, Lianns could control their own destinies. Flush with the potential, they went wild, tearing down old statues and monuments to the Empire.

They had much to deal with, however. The New Republic, though disappointed at their choice not to align with the new government, was willing to support their right to take that individual path. Taking the long view that sooner or later it would only make sense for Lianna to join their community, the Republic's officials figured they could afford to wait. The Empire, on the other hand, had never been so reasonable in the past and might not be so now.

Refusing the New Republic's offer of aid must have seemed suicidal at the time. Lord Verpalion was petitioning for Imperial troops to invade, but Lady Santhe wanted no favors from the former Rebels. The Old Republic hadn't done right by Lianna, and the New one wasn't even a sure thing yet. Many Lianns, some even in her own household, disagreed, but she held firm.

She had a special advantage she could use: the war itself. Short on equipment and ships, the Imperial Moff in the sector had no illusion about his chances if the supply of new TIE fighters was disrupted for any reason. Lady Santhe made it clear that Lianna would continue to supply TIE fighters provided it was left to its own devices. Reluctantly, the Moff agreed. A special charter of secession was granted. Of course, it made no mention of secret payments to Moff Gronn's coffers in order to prevent a military invasion, but Lady Santhe made it clear that if the Empire attempted to seize Lianna by force, the Lianns would use all of their weapons, including their vast research staff, to defend their world.

As part of a plan to refinance the company balance, Lady Santhe began an ambitious plan to remake Sienar. No longer would their product line be limited to spaceships. Everything from hand blasters to speeders to armor would soon carry the Santhe/Sienar logo (or that of one of its divisions) and buy freedom for her world. The first product of the new Santhe/Sienar is a compact assault vehicle, or mini-tank.

Nicknamed the Century tank, this is the first production model from Sienar Army Systems. Adapted from the cockpit of the TIE fighter (which Sienar makes), this tank allows a single trooper to have the effectiveness of a squad. Even the targeting computer for the medium blasters is similar to the one in TIE fighters. Since it can use many of the same interfaces as the TIE fighter, the TIE style tank is both economical to make and very easy to train troops to use.

■ Century Tank

Craft: Santhe/Sienar Technologies Century Tank
Type: Compact assault vehicle
Scale: Speeder
Length: 6.7 meters
Skill: Ground vehicle operation: Century tank
Crew: 1
Crew Skill: Vehicle blasters 5D, ground vehicle operation 5D+2
Passengers: 1
Cargo Capacity: 200 kilograms
Consumables: 5 days
Cover: Full
Cost: 37,000 credits
Maneuverability: 2D+1
Move: 30; 90KMH
Body Strength: 2D
Weapons:
  Two Medium Blaster Cannons
    Fire Arc: Front
    Skill: Vehicle blasters
    Fire Control: 2D
    Range: 50-400/900/2KM
    Damage: 5D
  Light Turbolaser
    Fire Arc: Turret
    Skill: Vehicle blasters
    Fire Control: 1D+2
    Range: 50-300/500/1KM
    Damage: 4D+1

Tank Droids

Compact assault vehicles (CAVs) have long been a tool of the Empire to maintain its control throughout the galaxy. Allowing one trooper to use the firepower of a whole squad, it was crucial to controlling the rioting that broke out across the huge urban metroplexes of the heavily populated Core and Colonies Regions. As successful as CAVs have proved during the long Civil War and Mutiny, in many situations there haven't been enough trained soldiers to make efficient use of them. As a cost cutting measure, it was decided to increase the number of battle robots to fill out the ranks of the Empire's ground vehicles.

Automated war machines have existed in the galaxy at least as long as Xim the Despot and his war droid army. The design of an effective sentient tank has been an ideal of Army planners for decades. Tireless, undistractable, implacable and adaptable to any situation without constant referral for updated orders, the tank droid has been one of the longest running projects for Imperial scientists. There were sophisticated automated perimeter bots in use by the Old Republic, but they were stationary units.

Most programmers had assumed that tank programming ought to be based on the "event pathstreaming" model, which is used for assassin droids. Tank droids based on this model never achieved the kind of long term independence and reliability to make the investment cost effective. Ground combat is very chaotic and the number of choices swamped the cognitive units. What was needed was a way to make the droid's brain self-motivating. In a rare reversal of fortune, a pirated pathway matrix from the New Republic's R7 Droid brain design gave them the needed independence factor.

The early prototypes were prohibitively expensive to mass produce. However, as the technology of the tank droids was refined, the machines eventually became inexpensive enough to mass produce for combat situations. This breakthrough happened during the time of Thrawn's return, but Thrawn's campaign drew attention from this new technology. It was only when Chief Engineer Umak Leth was called before the Emperor that this technology was pushed forward and onto the battlefield.

Leth contracted Arakyd, manufacturer of the infamous probe droid, to assemble these new weapons, the XR-85 Tank Droid. While there is only one type of tank droid in present use, the sophisticated brain of the machine could be adapted to any number of variants; it is quite likely that droid war machines will become a prime weapon of the modern battlefield.

■Tank Droid

Craft: Arakyd XR-85 Tank Droid
Type: Tank Droid
DEXTERITY 2D
Vehicle blasters 6D
KNOWLEDGE 1D
Urban warfare 2D
MECHANICAL 2D
Ground vehicle operation 6D
PERCEPTION 2D
Search 6D
STRENGTH 1D
TECHNICAL 1D
Scale: Walker
Length: 32 meters
Cost: 56,000 credits
Maneuverability: 1D+1
Move: 25; 70KMH
Body Strength: 6D

AS LASER BLASTS ECHO OFF THE CITY CANYON WALLS, HAN WORKS DESPERATELY TO CONTROL THE WILDLY CAREENING FLOATER--

HANG ON, YOUR WORSHIP--I'M TRYING TO FIGURE OUT THESE STRANGE KNOBS AND SWITCHES!

WHY IS IT YOU ALWAYS GET FORMAL WHEN YOU'RE ABOUT TO DO SOMETHING STUPID?

Weapons:
Heavy Particle Cannon
Fire Arc: Turret
Skill: Vehicle blasters
Fire Control: 2D
Range: 50-600/2/5KM
Damage: 6D
Two Light Turbolasers
Fire Arc: Front
Skill: Vehicle blasters
Fire Control: 1D
Range: 50-300/600/1KM
Damage: 4D+1
Four Twin Heavy Repeating blasters
Fire Arc: 2 front, 2 back
Scale: Speeder
Skill: Vehicle blasters
Fire Control: 2D
Range: 50-400/900/2KM
Damage: 5D
Golan Arms DF.9
Fire Arc: Back
Scale: Speeder
Skill: Vehicle blasters
Fire Control: 1D
Range: 20-500/800/1.2KM
Damage: 4D

Hutt Floaters

Hutts aren't exactly the most mobile of creatures, so it comes as no surprise that nearly all of them use some sort of craft to perform the most basic daily tasks. According to Hutt legend, even adults once moved about under their own power, but no modern Hutt would think of doing this today. They have come to dislike the act of physically clambering about so much that some have spent years without oozing sluggishly from one bit of furniture to another. So they are content to be carried about, as befits their status (or so they believe).

Folk stories are filled with fables about jeweled palanquins borne by several dozen slaves, or wheeled monstrosities lumbering through traffic. Now, the Hutt vehicle of choice (especially for Hutts who cannot afford a sail barge or other luxury craft) is the Hutt floater. Whole companies have sprung into existence to compete for this lucrative market. A Hutt's floater is a mark of his or her social status — the lowly, undecorated floater indicates a "wage slave" who is simply trying to survive. To Hutts, the gaudier the better, and this is reflected in their floaters. Owning fleets of floaters has become something of a mark of status in their circles.

The Nimbus Rider 2000 floater is one of the more "economical" floaters on the market, aimed at the less wealthy members of the Hutt population. While it can only fit one Hutt at a time (thus marking it as a "poor Hutt's" vehicle), one particular vehicle was more than enough for Han Solo and Princess Leia during their quick escape from Boba Fett.

■ Hutt Floater

Craft: Gefferon Nimbus Rider 2000
Type: Hutt Floater
Scale: Speeder
Length: 4 meters
Skill: Repulsorlift operation: Hutt floater
Crew: 1
Crew Skill: Varies according to individual
Passengers: None with Hutt; up to four Human-sized beings in lieu of Hutt
Cargo Capacity: 500 kilograms
Cover: 1/4
Altitude Range: Ground level – 30 meters
Cost: 25,000 credits (base model)
Maneuverability: 2D+1
Move: 25; 70KMH (loaded), 45; 130KMH (unloaded)
Body Strength: 1D+2

Amphibions

The Sedrians, in their short time with the Republic, have contributed much in terms of aquatic technologies. While they lagged far behind the Imperial standard, their nature allowed them to develop several amazing advances in the field of submarine and surface water technologies. One military application is the Republic Amphibion, manufactured by SedriMotors, Ltd. The vehicle proved vital in the Battle of Calamari.

Based around the chassis of an Incom XM-21 hydro-skiff, the Amphibion is a quiet, surface floater. It sits in the water and moves relatively slowly, but this is more than made up for by its quiet electric drives. The drives produce a light thrust and the vehicle hovers mere centimeters above the surface of the water. A traditional repulsorlift thruster can provide high speed travel as well, but the noise generated by such motors makes stealth attacks difficult. The Amphibion is difficult to hit because of its low profile and it offers cover for troops diving below.

■ Amphibion

Craft: SedriMotors Ltd. Amphibion
Type: Modified aquatic combat speeder
Scale: Speeder
Length: 7.3 meters
Skill: Hover vehicle operation: amphibion
Crew: 2, skeleton: 1/+5
Crew Skill: Vehicle blasters 5D, hover vehicle operation 4D+1
Passengers: 20 (troops)
Cargo Capacity: 200 kilograms
Cover: Full (crew), 1/2 (passengers)
Consumables: 3 days
Cost: 14,500 credits
Maneuverability: 1D+2
Move: 35; 100KMH
Body Strength: 2D+2
Weapons:
    Atgar 1.4 FD P-Tower (optional; mounted separately)
      Fire Arc: Turret
      Crew: 1
      Skill: Vehicle blasters

      Fire Control: 1D
      Range: 10-200/350/500
      Damage: 2D+2

Waveskimmer

The Waveskimmer is an effective dedicated aquatic combat vehicle. While not intended to replace the AT-AT swimmer, the Waveskimmer, or "Wave Walker", is most useful for augmenting an existing Imperial presence. The Waveskimmer is a surface craft allowing great speed and mobility.

The vehicle is based on an augmented AT-AT walker frame, although specially modified for water combat. The biggest difference is the propulsion system — the Waveskimmer is not a walker at all. The vehicle rests on two pontoon-like stabilizers on the ends of flattened booms. These booms are based on the same variable geometry servo-motors used in some snubfighters and the *Lambda*-class shuttle. The booms are equipped with micro-repulsorlift generators for stability, drive and maneuvering.

In the flattened position, the whole body floats on the surface of the water and troops can either drop directly through the bottom hatch to evade notice, or depart or unload equipment through a back cargo door.

When the Waveskimmer begins to move forward, the surface tension of the water creates a virtual solid surface, eliminating the instability suffered by traditional boats. The repulsor units keep it a few centimeters above the surface of the water.

As it gains speed, the support booms lock into position, lifting the whole body out of the water until only the pontoons are near the surface. This allows a great rate of speed. The vehicle has proven remarkably effective in assault duty.

■ Waveskimmer

Craft: Waveskimmer
Type: Attack hydrofoil
Scale: Walker
Length: 14 meters
Skill: Hover vehicle operation: Waveskimmer
Crew: 3, gunner: 2
Crew Skill: vehicle blasters 5D, walker operation 4D
Passengers: 28 (troops)
Cargo Capacity: 1 metric ton
Cover: Full
Cost: Not available for regular sale (285,000 credits on the Invisible Market)
Maneuverability: 1D
Move: 55; 160KMH
Body Strength: 3D
Weapons:
    Two Medium Blaster Cannons
      Fire Arc: 1 front/left*, 1 front/right*
      Crew: 1 (co-pilots)
      Skill: Vehicle blasters
      Fire Control: 1D+1

MOMENTS LATER, FAR BELOW, THE SECOND LINE OF DEFENSE EMERGES FROM THE FIERY BELLY OF EACH DEVASTATOR--

--FAST AND AGILE ATTACK SHIPS THAT BEGIN TO POUND THE REBEL AMPHIBIONS MERCILESSLY.

Range: 50-350/1/1.5KM
Damage: 4D
* The blaster cannon can only be turned to one facing per round.

Two Light Blaster Cannons
Fire Arc: 1 front, 1 back
Crew: 1
Skill: Vehicle blasters
Fire Control: 1D

Range: 50-300/500/1KM
Damage: 2D

Two Concussion Torpedo Launchers (fire-linked)
Fire Arc: Front
Crew: 1 (co-pilot)
Skill: Missile weapons
Fire Control: 1D
Range: 10-500/1/2KM
Damage: 3D

Chapter Nine
Equipment

Overview

Ingenuity Spawned of Warfare

The galaxy is experiencing a period of remarkable scientific discovery. This burst of creativity can be traced back to the earliest days of the Rebellion. The Empire controlled many technologies, especially those with military applications. The Alliance's personnel had to fight to counter Palpatine's limitless coffers. Short on equipment and money, they had to make do with what they could scrounge and jury-rig. As they did so, their ingenuity took over. At first, they only had ancient ships held together with spit and magnastaples, but as the Rebels grew more confident and capable, their tools and equipment became more impressive. They built dockyards, reopened forgotten mines, and built hydroponic farms. They adapted.

Their efforts, and the freedom the galaxy experienced under the New Republic, stimulated the lapsed spirit of discovery. The galaxy is being reborn into a new age of dynamism.

Universal Energy Cage

During the Great Purge of the Jedi Knights, it was much easier to capture them than to keep them imprisoned. Imperial Dungeon Ships had elaborate and expensive means to keep Jedi under control, but once they arrived at the Emperor's strongholds, transporting them safely from the ships proved dangerous. The Jedi often used their Force powers to break free. More guards weren't the answer since a clever Jedi could trick them or create a distraction.

Some way had to be found to keep even the most powerful Jedi Master from escaping. At the time, a Junior Engineer named Umak Leth put

AN ENERGIZED CAGE IS WAITING -- A TRAP TO HOLD A *JEDI!*

his mind to the matter. Working from the little information the Emperor gave him about the nature of the Force, he came to realize that the Force was an energy field. Rather than block it, it would be more efficient to disrupt it with more energy, he reasoned.

The result was the Universal Energy Cage. It could hold dangerous prisoners of any kind, not just Force Adepts. The cage is being used in more and more situations across the galaxy. The cage is a floating confinement sphere, three meters in diameter, filled with elaborate coils of superconductors overlapping in a complex pattern. Once energized, the whole sphere is wrapped in a force field, similar to the ones used to contain ionized plasmas in reactors; the force field seals the occupant within.

The unit moves by use of a repulsorlift unit and it suspends the prisoner within the cage with a secondary repulsorlift unit. The more a prisoner attempts to break out, the more feedback they receive. The sphere is entirely self-contained and floats through the air so no one can sabotage it. The only way to unlock the cage is through a specially coded radio signal held only by the Sovereign Protectors.

It is currently unknown what the specific limitations of the energy cage are, how strong a prisoner it could hold, how long it could hold them or if any sort of energy dampener could break through the field.

■ Universal Energy Cage

Model: Imperial Universal Energy Cage
Type: Enclosed prisoner transfer system
Scale: Character
Cost: 100,000 credits
Availability: X (restricted to legal governments)
Move: 15; 45KMH
Game Notes: Energy cage encloses prisoner in a force field with a *Strength* of up to 15D (unit only applies as much energy as necessary to restrain prisoner, so the energy level is often much lower when not being resisted). Somehow, the cage emanates a special type of energy that blocks Force energies and similar mental energies with an effectiveness of up to 15D. The unit has a special repulsor unit keeping the prisoner suspended in the center of the cage. This bottom mounted unit also supplies oxygen to the prisoner (there are no provisions for food and water; it is presumed that a Jedi will go into hibernation if he or she spends a long time in the cage).

Cloning

Cloning is a science of infamy and horror to most citizens of the galaxy due to the pain of the Clone Wars. In the past year, the Republic has had to deal with two separate instances of cloning: first, the clone warriors of Grand Admiral Thrawn's armada; second, the Emperor's newfound ability to occupy cloned bodies of himself. This long-banned technology has nearly resulted in the overthrow of the Republic.

Cloning takes a Human cell, and duplicates its genetic code. The code is implanted in a cell and as the cell grows into a Human, it will create an exact duplicate of the cell donor. To prevent any outside influence, the clones gestate in vats or Spaarti cylinders — mechanical wombs filled with nutrient chemicals and organic catalyzers. By varying the composition of the nutrient bath, it is possible to alter the clone to enhance certain physical characteristics and by increasing the catalyzer solution, growth can be accelerated many times. Under the right conditions, a full grown adult body can be produced in a few weeks, as demonstrated by Thrawn. Of course, one of the reasons why cloning was abandoned is that many clones were mentally unstable. While theories vary on this, some speculate that clones interfere with natural life forces. It seems that Thrawn's use of the ysalamiri overcame this obstacle.

While useful for spawning identical physical specimens on a huge scale, the downside is that the clones are without the personality of the original. They must be taught everything from scratch. Since environment is equally important to the development of the clone, individual clones, while starting out as genetically identical, may develop diverging and distinct identities.

The key to Palpatine's immortality is the growth of new bodies to replace his present one. As each successive body is destroyed and shriveled by the power of the Dark Side, Palpatine must force his life essence into new clone bodies. Palpatine's experimentations with cloning date back many years — he revealed to Luke Skywalker that he had inhabited many clone bodies prior to his "death" over Endor. In time, his scientists perfected his base genetic patterns to create bodies with enhanced intelligence, stamina, strength and agility.

This is where the Emperor's Dark Side skill comes into play. Just as he can siphon off the vital life force of his subjects on Byss, he can will his own personality, his very life, into a waiting receptacle body. Because the clones are one step removed from the natural life process itself, they are much more vulnerable to the effects of the Dark Side, aging at an extremely accelerated rate. Therefore, Palpatine grows many more at the same time as back ups.

While the clone body matures, the Clone Vats introduce special polymer chains to the nutrient cylinder. Combining with the skin, the polymer forms a tough fibrous membrane that covers and protects the body during the decanting phase. This mottled second skin is eventually sloughed off.

Planetary Shields

Planetary shields have long been a staple of warfare. Powered by reactors or giant solar arrays, the most powerful shields can stop nearly any type of assault, from an artificial asteroid shower to outright bombardment by military fleets. Most planetary shields are powerful enough to stop any ship from passing through them.

Planetary shields are collections of individual shield projectors. The final form is a series of overlapping individual shields. The actual defensive value of shields can vary immensely, depending upon available energy, quality of technology and a number of other factors. Additionally, few planetary governments can afford to wrap an entire planet in energy shields; instead, shields are established over vital targets so that they escape direct bombardment. As a result, air and ground forces must often drop beyond the range of the shield and then attack the target.

Of course, as shields developed, more powerful weapons were developed to try to overcome these shields. Examples of this are the Empire's awesome torpedo spheres, whose sole purpose is to seek out weaknesses in planetary shields and destroy them. The torpedo spheres and similar dedicated siege platforms use extensive sensor webs to probe the whole fabric of a shield, sometimes for hours at a time. When a weakness is found, tractor beams can be tuned to resonate on the weak frequency. The spheres launch several waves of proton torpedoes to crumble the shield and leave the planet at the mercy of the Empire.

The superlaser, main weapon of the Death Star and the Imperial flagship *Eclipse,* takes another tack. Instead of weakening a shield, the superlaser is able to pierce through it by using a coupled neutrino charge. This neutrino charge not only plunges through the shield, but it penetrates the mantle and lower levels of the planet. Great chunks of the crust can be vaporized, sometimes sending the surface exploding outward with enough force to shatter the world.

■ Planetary Shields
Model: Hibomehrt-Wyrrgex DefenStar 5000
Type: Planetary shield relay system
Scale: Death Star
Skill: Planetary shields
Crew: 150, skeleton: 50/+15
Crew Skill: Planetary shields 6D
Cost: 500,000 credits per shield
Availability: X
Game Notes: Each shield protects a 100 square kilometer area. The shield provides 6D Death Star-scale protection. Anything that hits the shield suffers 6D damage; energy bolts hitting the shields make opposed damage rolls. If the planetary shield's roll is higher the energy bolt is snuffed. If the energy bolt's roll is higher, for every 6 points by which the bolt exceeds the shield roll, 1D of damage passes through; additionally, the shield system takes damage as per normal combat results. If the shield system is damaged, the system has 5D of backup shields that can be brought on-line with a Moderate *planetary shields* roll. The shield system has a fire control of 3D. Each shield must have its own power generator.
Notes On Planets: A typical habitable planet has a structural rating of 10D-20D (Death Star scale). Alderaan had no shields of any kind, so it was utterly vaporized. A shielded planet that is overcome by a superlaser may "merely" have its entire surface burned off or split into several pieces. Note that planets don't have to be destroyed to be rendered uninhabitable.

Droids

Ubiquitous and hardworking, droids are the invisible support for the economy of the galaxy. Invisible because so few pay any attention to them. Considering how many there are in use proves just how important they are to the galaxy's quality of life: on some worlds, the droid population outnumbers the organic by a factor of 14 to one. Even the poorest moisture farm can afford a few clunky treadwells to keep the vaporators and catalyzers running to perfection.

Droids have nearly replaced most unskilled and much skilled labor throughout the galaxy. Droids are much more than mere ambulatory computers: part of what makes the droid so useful is its high intelligence, allowing it to adapt to new situations and giving it a limited ability to interpret confusing commands.

The final factor in smoothly integrating droids into the galactic economy is that droids are given personality. These personalities can become quite elaborate over time. Of course, droids are still property and aren't accorded individual rights. Some owners wipe a droid's memory periodically to prevent the development of personality. Still many, especially those in the New Republic, have come to look on droids as people instead of machines. Most in the Republic will never forget that their very survival once depended on a pair of droids.

ZZ-4Z (ZeeZee)

ZeeZee is a very old droid indeed, but he doesn't mind, as long as he can keep everything the way it ought to be; the way the Master wishes it. One of the last of a rapidly outpaced model series, he is a housekeeping droid, designed to maintain and repair the private residences of wealthy and important citizens. Nowadays, most house maintenance is taken care of by small servomechs that can pop out and disappear once the work is done while the owner's attention is elsewhere.

A few centuries ago, however, the idea of having a humanoid "Gentlebeings'Droid" was all the rage among the nouveau riche and Serv-O-Droid first marketed the JV-Z1 model to tap into this fad. Tireless and obsequious, housekeeping droids are only rivaled by the famed protocol droids from Cybot Galactica for their superciliousness enhancement subroutines. They rarely functioned alone, but were the coordinators for a whole household of droids including chefbots, auto-chauffeurs and cleaning droids. The major-domo could be programmed to remember the most excruciatingly household procedures and faultlessly keep everything running for years without further instruction.

In the case of ZeeZee, he was programmed as the private secretary for the Dean of the Spacers Academy. He had been willed to the Academy by an eccentric and anonymous donor "in the hopes that the Deans may never forget the civility which all citizens must hold dear." ZeeZee had served over 17 Deans and could affectionately rattle off the peculiar quirks and habits of each one. ZeeZee was quite popular with the cadets, who never tired of learning embarrassing trivia. ZeeZee was released from service by Dean Horace Wyrmyr. He didn't quite like droids and kept ordering ZeeZee to go off on pointless errands when all ZeeZee wanted was to make life easier for him. As major domo of the Dean's Residence, he had access to all of Wyrmyr's secrets.

One day, ZeeZee found he had made a friend. His friend was a most unusual Human by the name of Mako Spince, and Mako was very curious about Dean Wyrmyr. Unknown to anyone but the two, it was ZeeZee who took the control codes to the physics lab where Mako stole the antimatter for his "final" prank. When Wyrmyr learned of this, he went berserk and sent the droid to the recycling plants. Following Spince's expulsion, Mako droid-napped the housekeeper as a final gesture.

Soon, ZeeZee's endless bantering grew to annoy even Mako, so he intentionally lost a sabacc game just to get him off his hands. The lucky man to win him was none other than Han Solo, smuggler extraordinaire.

Imagine ZeeZee's surprise when he got his first orders on the

HI, ZEEZEE...

GOSH, I SEE YOU DID A *GREAT JOB* OF TAKING CARE OF THE PLACE WHILE I WAS GONE!

MR. *SOLO*... SO... kik... GOOD TO... kik... kik.

FZT... A MR. FETT TO SEE YOU, SIR...

FZT... A MR. FETT TO SEE YOU, SIR...

FZT... A MR. FETT TO SEE YOU, SIR...

MISTER *WHO?* WHAT THE--

management of Solo's garret, "I dunno, just leave it all … just like this." ZeeZee was nothing if not obedient, and so he has always kept it just as it was that day. Of course, Han complained when ZeeZee tried to stop Han from reusing the socks off the floor. He had just bought Han a whole new wardrobe to replace the ones he'd glued to the floor anyway; they worked it all out eventually.

Characteristically, Han's fast exit from Nar Shaddaa left him little time to tie up loose ends. In the rush, ZeeZee was all but forgotten. ZeeZee waited. Mr. Solo would be so pleased, especially with his old friend Mr. Fett coming by so often to check up on things. There was that bit about a blaster fight, but then organics were a peculiar breed. It remains to be seen whether Han will ever return to repair ZeeZee, but his wife has commented that it couldn't hurt to have a droid around the house — and besides, he and Threepio would probably hit it off.

■ ZZ-4Z (ZeeZee)

Type: JV-Z1/D Housekeeping Droid
DEXTERITY 1D
KNOWLEDGE 2D
Accounting 7D, bureaucracy 6D, cultures 5D+2
MECHANICAL 1D
Household appliance operation 8D
PERCEPTION 2D
Search 5D
STRENGTH 1D
Cleaning 7D, lifting 5D
TECHNICAL 3D
Equipped With:
• Humanoid body (two arms, two legs)
• Internal database
• Infrared Lintscope
• Vocabulator

Hunter-Killer Probot

Contrary to what their appearance might suggest, the Hunter-Killer is more than just an oversized probot. They are highly intelligent pursuit and detainment vehicles.

An attempt to take up the slack of reduced availability of organic forces, H-Ks patrol hazardous regions of the Empire. They also find use in police actions and as a blockade perimeter defense droid, both in systems and on planets. Groups of these are often slaved together by an Imperial Customs Frigate (when in deep space), or by an Imperial Patrol Vessel (when in orbital patrol patterns). No matter the situation, the Hunter-Killer is a very unwelcome sight to most smugglers.

The H-K mounts very powerful sensors including special penetrating hullscanners that allow the H-K to get a limited view inside the cargo space of a suspicious freighter. If there is the slightest possibility of contraband, the H-K can search the ship with its other dedicated sensors. These include graphiscan recognition codes that can identify over 11,000 planetary and national registries and can cross reference to spot likely forgeries.

One of the largest combat-capable droids, the Hunter-Killer easily lives up to its name with its fully integrated offensive and defensive armament programs, which allow it to coordinate with up to a dozen others. The H-K also features a "containment chamber." Once a smuggler has been identified and cross-confirmed by the supervisory vessel, it can immobilize the prey with its ion cannon. Then it uses tractor beams to pull the unfortunate ship into the armored chamber, swallowing its prey whole.

■ Hunter-Killer Probot

Type: Arakyd Hunter-Killer Probot
DEXTERITY 3D
Dodge 5D
KNOWLEDGE 2D+2
Bureaucracy 3D, law enforcement: Imperial customs procedures 6D
MECHANICAL 3D
Starship gunnery 5D, starship shields 5D
PERCEPTION 4D
Search 7D
STRENGTH 2D
TECHNICAL 2D+2
Scale: Capital
Size: 150 meters tall
Cost: 165,000 credits
Space: 3
Atmosphere: 105; 300KMH
Shields: 1D
Hull: 4D
Equipped With:
• 4 heavy grasping extensors (+2D to *lifting*)
• 4 fine work grasping extensors
• Advanced sensor array:
  Passive: 40/2D
  Scan: 80/2D+2
  Search: 100/3D+1
  Focus: 5/4D+2
• Capture system including:
  One Tractor Beam Projector
  Fire Arc: Front
  Space Range: 1-5/15/30
  Atmosphere Range: 100-500/1.5/3KM
  Damage: 5D
• Internal secure chamber. Large enough to hold a light freighter (30 meters by 30 meters by 10 meters tall).
• **Weapons:**
  Two Quad Blaster cannons (fire-linked)
  Fire Arc: Turret
  Skill: Starship gunnery
  Space Range: 1-5/10/17
  Atmosphere Range: 100-500/1/1.7KM
  Damage: 4D+1
  Two Ion Cannon
  Fire Arc: Turret
  Skill: Starship gunnery
  Space Range: 1-3/7/36
  Atmosphere Range: 100-300/700/3.6KM
  Damage: 8D

The Final Chapter!

LAST COMMAND
S O U R C E B O O K

September 1993

WEST
END
GAMES ®

RR3 Box 2345 ▪ Honesdale, PA 18431